To Boo, who once said:
"If you love it so much, why don't you write
about it?"

The Wrong-Way Comet and Other Mysteries of Our Solar System

Essays by Barry Evans
Foreword by Dr. Frank Drake
President, SETI Institute

TAB BOOKS
Blue Ridge Summit, PA

Trademarks
Bic®　　　　　Bic Corporation
Freon®　　　　du Pont de Nemours & Co. Ltd.
Frisbee®　　　Wham-O Manufacturing Co.
Ping-Pong®　 Parker Bros.

FIRST EDITION
FIRST PRINTING

© 1992 by **TAB Books**.
TAB Books is a division of McGraw-Hill, Inc.

Library of Congress Cataloging-in-Publication Data

Evans, Barry.
　　The wrong-way comet and other mysteries of our solar system :
　essays / by Barry Evans.
　　　p.　　cm.
　　Includes index.
　　ISBN 0-8306-2679-4　　　ISBN 0-8306-2670-0 (pbk.)
　　1. Solar system.　I. Title.　II. Title: The fourteen-mile high
　volcano and other wonders of the solar system.
　QB501.E89　1992
　523.2—dc20　　　　　　　　　　　　　　　　　　91-34004
　　　　　　　　　　　　　　　　　　　　　　　　　　CIP

TAB Books offers software for sale. For information and a catalog, please
contact TAB Software Department, Blue Ridge Summit, PA 17294-0850.

Acquisitions Editor: Roland S. Phelps
Book Editor: Melanie D. Brewer
Director of Production: Katherine G. Brown
Book Design: Jaclyn J. Boone
Cover Illustration: Margaret Brandt, Harrisburg, PA
Cover Design: Lori E. Schlosser　　　　　　　　　　　　　　　　EL1

Contents

Foreword

It was 1959 when I had my first exciting encounter with the remarkable subject of this book, the solar system. Fresh out of graduate school, I had the privilege of being one of the first astronomers to use the newly established National Radio Astronomy Observatory in Green Bank, West Virginia. Earth-orbiting *Sputnik* had launched the space age just two years before, but the voyages of interplanetary spacecraft were years in the future. It is hard to believe now, but in those days the studies of the planets and satellites of our system was a taboo subject. "Real" astronomers did not engage in observations of objects so low on the celestial totem pole. To do so was an admission of inferiority and a threat to a person's career.

I was tantalized by some peculiar detections of radio emissions, made at the Naval Research Laboratory, from Venus and Jupiter. Being young and brash, with little respect for the growlings of old fuddy-duddies, I trained the first of our new Green Bank radio telescopes on those two planets. The power of that telescope took me through the looking glass, revealing a solar system far more complex than we had ever imagined. Those observations showed that the temperature on Venus was very hot: about 800 degrees Fahrenheit. Later I made one of the longest observations ever, 80 hours, to detect the radio power from the *night* side of Venus. We then discovered that even the night side had the same prodigious temperature, telling us that the atmosphere of the planet was a blanket of undreamed thickness. And when we pointed the telescope at Jupiter, we detected radio emission levels hundreds of times greater than expected. The spectrum of these emissions was exactly the one observed in Earth's Van Allen Belts, where high energy electrons orbit in magnetic fields, but Jupiter's belts had millions of times more particles than Earth's. As a result of these discoveries, my career was not set back after all. The solar system was a gold mine of fascinating phenomena. I thought, "Why not send spacecraft to the planets?" And in time we did.

Those early discoveries not only showed how diverse and unpredictable the universe is, they also established that we were justified in pursuing provocative and unpopular scientific ideas. One that I particularly cherished was the possibility of the existence of other advanced civilizations in space. We realized that we could detect duplicates of our radio signals being sent from Earth, if such signals were sent from civilizations accompanying nearby stars. Buoyed by our successes with detection of natural radio emissions in the solar system, I proposed a search for *intelligent* radio signals from the two nearest sun-like stars. Fortunately, the leaders of the observatory were pioneers at heart, and they quickly agreed to the project.

"Project Ozma" began in the spring of 1960. For 200 hours, we searched for signals from hypothetical planets of the nearby stars Tau Ceti and Epsilon Eridani with a sensitive radio receiver that could monitor only one frequency at a time. We listened in the vicinity of 1420 megahertz, the fundamental radiation of the hydrogen atom, reasoning that that would be a cosmic "meeting place," because hydrogen is by far the most abundant element in the universe. (Fortuitously, building the equipment for this frequency meant that it could be used for conventional research, thus heading off any accusations that we were wasting resources.) We found nothing, which was neither surprising nor discouraging, and after our search, the telescope continued a long and successful career of more conventional astronomical observations.

This was the first search for extraterrestrial intelligence, or SETI. Many others followed. The growth in search capability has been amazing: it has been steady for some thirty years, with the power of searches doubling every 200 days or so, with no end or obstacle in sight. More importantly, the search has been joined by many of the world's most talented scientists. NASA has committed over 100 million dollars towards the search. We have even *sent* messages: in 1974 we used the giant Arecibo radio telescope to send a message that could be detected by a similar instrument at the farthest fringes of the Milky Way.

Today, we are poised on the threshold of a giant step in our search for creatures like ourselves. The growing enthusiasm and support for this venture, perhaps the most important project in science, results in part from recent discoveries in our own solar system—the subject of this book—which strongly support my belief that life is abundant in the universe.

We have now taken a close look at more than forty major objects in the solar system. Whereas once we thought we might find mainly similarities, instead we have found differences; every one has some special features that tantalize us, and often enlighten us. Who would have imagined, for example, that one of the major satellites of Jupiter, Europa, would be covered with an ice-covered ocean of water? Or that another of those satellites, Io, so far from the warmth of the sun, would be wracked almost continually by erupting volcanoes? Or that at the very edge of the solar system, where the sun is but a bright star in the sky, Neptune's satellite Triton would be spewing material into its dark sky from volcanoes and geysers?

On the surfaces of the planets and satellites, and in the comets and meteorites, we have not only read the history of the solar system, but we have also glimpsed possible futures, particularly for our planet. We have seen that throughout the entire history of the system, every object has been subjected to bombardment by large objects, often with catastrophic results. We now know that the evolution of life on Earth has been strongly influenced by the effects of these projectiles. Indeed, the impact that occurred about 65 million years ago seems to have caused the demise of so many large predators that our planet became a place where the tiny mammals of that time could flourish to become, in time, the humans of today. The bombardment is not over; even in this century we have seen a could-have-been catastrophic impact that was almost harmless only because it occurred in the only place where catastrophe was not inevitable: Siberia. We must learn more about these speeding projectiles in the solar system, and protect ourselves from them.

Not only is the solar system intriguing, it is also remarkably beautiful: the great swirling cloud patterns on Jupiter, the geometric ring system of Saturn, (seen properly only from the Voyager spacecraft), the royal blue of Neptune. Then there are the great volcanoes on Mars, some so large they would stretch from Oregon to Mexico, and a canyon so great that it would reach from the Atlantic to the Pacific if it were on Earth. Miranda, a moon of Uranus with a patchwork of exotic terrains, sports a cliff ten miles high. Anything dropped from this cliff would take five minutes to fall to the bottom.

And everywhere, we are tantalized by hints of life-now, in the past, or life to be. The meandering stream beds of Mars, where water must have flowed, evoke the question: did creatures once swim against these currents, as they now do on Earth? Jupiter and Saturn reveal clouds of brownish and reddish hues, evidence of atmospheres rich in carbon compounds related to the chemicals of life. Could life exist on Saturn's giant satellite, Titan, which has a dense organic-rich atmosphere? And what of that material spewing forth from the geysers of Triton? Its color, too, is reminiscent of the color of the basic materials from which we think life springs.

With so many hints of primitive life found in the solar system, is life—even advanced life—a common commodity in the universe? Our discoveries in the solar system have served as an inspiration for SETI (Search for Extra Terrestrial Intelligence) and for the greatest pursuit yet. Radio searches are already underway in Massachusetts and Argentina with systems that monitor almost ten million different radio frequency channels at a time. In October of 1992, 500 years after the first voyage of Columbus, a powerful NASA search will begin monitoring about 15 million frequency channels at once. It will cover the entire sky for signals, with particularly good sensitivity to be used on about one thousand nearby sun-like stars. The search will use sophisticated computer techniques to test the observations—fifteen million numbers a second!—for a variety of types of signals, and in its first few *hours* will have accomplished more than all our previous searches put together. Perhaps by the turn of the century, or even sooner if we are lucky, we will know that answer to that age-old question: Are there intelligent creatures elsewhere in the universe?

SETI is a natural outgrowth of our discoveries in that scientific treasure chest which is our solar system. In Barry Evans' book you'll find some of the shiniest jewels from that chest, sparkling beyond even our wildest dreams of thirty years ago.

Frank Drake
President, SETI Institute

Acknowledgments

This is my first book. These days I walk into bookstores and look around in awe, because I have now a taste of what writing a book entails. This one certainly has had its share of midwives and helpmates, and I'm hugely grateful in particular to the following:

For technical advice and/or reviews: Chris McKay, David Morrison, and Scott Sanford (NASA-Ames Research Center); Bob Wagoner (Stanford University); Frank Drake (University of California, Santa Cruz); and Seth Shostak (SETI Institute); Mark Robinson (University of Hawaii); and William Phelps and Dan Farley.

For assistance with graphics: Astrophotographer Gèrard Therin; Artists Mike Carroll and Don Davis; Steve Mezaros for the planetary comparisons; Laura Eisner of Tom Van Sant's Geosphere Project (which in turn acknowledges NOAA, NASA, Eyes on Earth, and Lloyd Van Warren); Jurrie van der Woude (JPL); Scott Hildreth and Andy Fralknoi (Astronomical Society of the Pacific); and the Biblioteca Nazionale Centrale, Florence, Italy.

For inspiration: Paul Boynton (University of Washington).

For giving my monthly astronomy column StarWatch *its start:* Jack Keith and the Bellingham Herald.

For flying us safely to the 1991 eclipse: Gert Eberlein.

For believing in this: Roland Phelps, TAB/McGraw-Hill.

For sanity in a caring environment: All at Gondolyn.

And for the wonder of it all: Sarah Louisa Rogers.

Introduction

How can anyone learn anything new who does not find it a shock?
J. A. Wheeler, *A Journey into Gravity and Spacetime*

We live in an exciting neighborhood. As you read about it in this book, I hope you get to experience at least a few shocks. Once, *neighborhood* meant the streets around our home. As our perspective broadened, the concept enlarged, first to communities, then to whole regions, and today we speak of the global neighborhood. The neighborhood of this book takes the concept one step further, into nearby space, the space we've visited during the last thirty years via our surrogate spacecraft. This book is about our cosmic neighborhood, the solar system.

It's designed for two levels of readers. If you're a raw beginner in astronomy, you'll find this book accessible, friendly, and easy to understand. If you've been following astronomy for a while, you'll already know what an intoxicating subject it is. You'll find plenty in here—especially some of the newer discoveries about the solar system—to take you to new levels of intoxication.

The book is divided into six chapters, each containing about ten essays. My goal has been to allow each essay to stand by itself, so you can dip in and out of the book at will. For trivia-fans, several miscellanies are included, and a glossary defines most of the scientific terms used. The six chapters are summarized below.

Chapter 1, *Setting the stage*, outlines the vast scales of our cosmic neighborhood and offers tools to understand it in terms of both space and time. The chapter also introduces gravity, the dominant force at astronomical scales.

Chapter 2, *The sun, our local atomic power station*, explains what the sun is and how it works. You'll learn how discovering the sun's atomic secrets led to the invention of the hydrogen bomb.

Chapter 3, *Earth and moon*, looks at the moon's formation and its influence on us, together with new ways of seeing our own Earth. Eclipses are featured, in particular the great 1991 solar eclipse.

Chapter 4, *The inner planets*, is about Mercury, Venus, and Mars, with particular emphasis on next-door Mars: why it's a prime candidate for exploration and transformation into a habitable planet.

Chapter 5, *The outer planets*, takes a tour to the highlights of Jupiter, Saturn, Uranus, Neptune, and Pluto. Voyager, the Little Spacecraft that Could, is given special mention.

Chapter 6, *Comets, asteroids, and meteors*, discusses the minor members of our solar system. It also offers new answers to that venerable question: What happened to the dinosaurs?

An appendix, *Viewing the nearby heavens*, encourages you to get out there with binoculars and look at the neighborhood cosmic bodies, especially the moon.

Much of the book is loosely based on a syndicated monthly column I've been writing for the past five years, StarWatch. It appears in 30-odd newspapers large and small across the U.S. As with my columns, I've attempted in this book to follow Einstein's precept for the presentation of scientific subjects: Make it as simple as it can be, and no simpler.

This is far from a comprehensive overview of the solar system. Rather, it's an attempt to evoke in people with little or no scientific background some of the same spirit of wonder that I see in even the most serious of astronomers. After all, astronomers are scientists, and what are scientists but adult-looking girls and boys who have never been able to stop playing?

Clear skies!

Barry Evans
Palo Alto, California, February, 1992

1
Setting the stage

Astronomy is really a branch of psychology. We're building a card castle, climbing a ladder to the stars through inductive logic. The fact that the Andromeda galaxy is more than two million light-years away does not really excite me. It's the fact that you and I can presume to know that fact!

Ashley McDermott, astronomer

We live on the surface of a planet bound by gravity to the sun, along with eight other planets, many moons, and other small bodies. We call the whole complex the solar system. This is part of our galaxy, the Milky Way, one of billions of galaxies in the universe as a whole.

As part of the universe, the solar system is dominated by three aspects: space, time, and gravity. Space and time give us a sense of where and when we are, while gravity rules the motion of this planet and everything else of any size in the universe.

In this section, we'll set the stage for what follows. The depths of space and time are so fantastic that it's easy to dismiss phrases like "thousands of light years" and "billions of years" as mere poetry—words on the page that defy visceral understanding. Yet that's what understanding is in this context: a visceral experience. Not only do I want you to experience the enormities of the spatial and temporal frameworks of the solar system and the galaxy to which it belongs, I want you to be in awe of them.

The solar system I learned about as a boy was a cozy little neighborhood in the sky. Earth was a lumbering beach ball of a planet not too different in size from Jupiter, the largest planet with which we share our home star, the sun. Indeed, the sun itself wasn't that big, and we weren't all that far away from it. Somehow, my youthful mental picture had space as quite busy: the spaces between planets were filled with comets and dust, asteroids and, I dare say, spaceships. That was the age of Dan Dare, England's stoic version of Flash Gordon. Then, even trips to the stars were minor inconveniences, a couple of extra Warp Factors away from local interplanetary jaunts. In short, my childhood universe was safe, small, and tightly-packed with *stuff*.

This section of the book, however, is not about the way it was for me—and perhaps for you. It's about how it actually is, as best as twentieth century science can understand. It's about emptiness and remoteness in space and time. I suppose it's also about loneliness.

The bare facts are these: our home is the surface of an unimaginably small rocky ball which, with its neighbor the moon, is far away—millions of miles—from the closest planets. We orbit a star trillions upon trillions of miles distant from its nearest neighbor. And our star is one of a few hundred billion making up our home galaxy, the Milky Way, which is one galaxy of billions.

Millions, billions, trillions. What can we do with these numbers to make them come alive? In this section, we'll try to understand both the very large and the very small. We'll use the tiny atom, constituent of everything we can see and touch, to help us experience the relative scale of things. Actually *feeling* the vast difference in size between atoms and ourselves will help us make a similar transition from our daily world to the scale of the solar system and its place in the galaxy.

New kids on the block

What is true of space—that it's fearsomely large—is also true of time. We live in a universe that, according to most astronomers, had a beginning some 15 billion years back in time (the Big Bang). The first life on Earth dates from nearly four billion years ago, and our mammalian ancestors from just two hundred million years ago. We're the new kids on the block, and we'll try to get a gut-level feel for what that means.

What runs it all? Gravity—the only one of the four known forces that has a significant effect on anything much larger than an atom. Planets in their orbits, stars in their galaxies, nebulae and black holes, are all ruled by gravity. It's pulling you down in your chair right now. Yet gravity is an illusory beast, a unicorn that Einstein said is really a manifestation of the "web of spacetime," rather than forces acting at distances like invisible cosmic rubber bands. By getting at least a feel for the difference, you'll understand a little better how the solar system works.

Space, time, and gravity. This is the stuff of our first section. This is where, when, and why it's all happening—the stage of the cosmos.

Millions, billions and trillions

Scientists and engineers who know the difference between a part per million and a part per billion have a public duty to become active in policy-making.

John Sununu, former presidential chief-of-staff

We'll be using some large numbers in this book. Let's spend a couple of minutes at the outset looking at these numbers to see how we can make sense of them. We'll look at two tricks to make these numbers meaningful: converting them into seconds and equating them with grains of sand.

Here are the numeric expressions used in the United States and Canada. (It's different in Great Britain.)

1 million = 1,000,000 or 10^6 (the superscript or power *6* indicates one followed by six zeros)

1 billion = 1,000,000,000 or 10^9

1 trillion = 1,000,000,000,000 or 10^{12}

Counting in seconds

Count to yourself, using a watch if you need to, so that the time it takes you to say each number is equivalent to about one second.

- A million equals about 12 days of seconds. Think of what you were doing 12 days ago and imagine that you've been counting since then.
- A billion equals about 32 years of seconds. If you're 32 years old and you started counting when you were born, you'd have arrived at about one billion today.
- A trillion equals about 32,000 years of seconds—about the elapsed time since our Neanderthal cousins became extinct.

Counting in sand

Sand can be used as another useful conversion for us to grasp large numbers. To a geologist, sand is a particle of rock having a diameter more than 0.0625 and smaller than 2.000 millimeters (25.4 millimeters equal one inch). To us, sand is what you find on a sandy beach, neither particularly fine nor coarse. About 10 million grains fit in each cubic foot. Try to picture these equivalences (Fig. 1-1):

- One million grains of sand would fill two-thirds of a shoe box
- One billion grains of sand would fill a hot tub
- One trillion grains of sand, piled 21 inches deep, would fit onto a football field.

Astronomical units and light years

The *astronomical unit*, or AU, is a convenient unit of length when we're dealing with the solar system. One AU is the mean distance of Earth from the sun, nearly 93 million miles away. This unit makes it easier to picture how far other planets are from the sun. For example, Jupiter is about 5 AU from the sun, while Pluto, usually the most distant planet, has a mean distance of nearly 40 AU.

Light years are often used to discuss cosmic distances. Light doesn't travel instantaneously; it takes time to get anywhere. For instance, it takes light 1¼ seconds to travel to the moon, one quarter of a million miles away; and a little over 8 minutes to reach us from the sun, 93 million miles away. We say the distance to the moon is 1¼ light seconds, and to the sun 8 light minutes.

The closest star (other than the sun) is Proxima Centauri, about 4¼ light years away. Light that left there on January 1, 1990, arrives here in the middle of March, 1994. It's actually about 25 trillion miles away, but the term light year is more convenient.

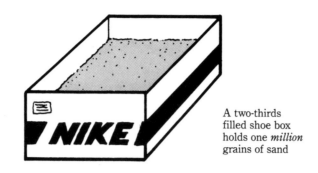

A two-thirds filled shoe box holds one *million* grains of sand

A small hot tub (six feet diameter, three-and-a-half feet deep) holds one *billion* grains of sand

Sand placed 21 inches deep on a football field: one *trillion* grains

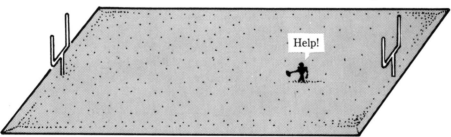

1-1 Counting in sand: How we can use the number of grains of sand in familiar objects to get a feel for large numbers.

The size of the atom

Not exist? Not exist? Why, I can see the little buggers as plain as I can see that spoon in front of me!

Ernest Rutherford, New Zealand physicist, about 1920. Response to British physicist Arthur Eddington's remark over dinner at Cambridge that If electrons were so unimaginably small, perhaps they didn't exist except as mental concepts.

The universe is very big and we're very small. We are actually somewhere in the middle between the biggest and smallest that nature has to offer. By getting a sense of the very small, we can extend our understanding of that to the very large. So we'll start off with what's arguably the smallest object—the electron. From there we'll go to the electron's giant cousin, the proton, and then to the arbiter of the sun's energy source, the atom itself.

The electron

The story goes that an elderly senator, who had been listening intently to a scientific presentation at a formal hearing, asked, "Is an electron that much smaller than a speck of dust?" The answer was, "Senator, an electron bears the same relation to a speck of dust as a speck of dust does to the size of the earth."

When I heard this, my reaction was "Wow!" My mind boggled. I told a couple of friends and found boggled minds easy to come by. Then reality set in. "I didn't think electrons had any size," said one of them. "How can your ratios possibly be true?"

Fair enough question. Despite Rutherford's cheerful vision of electrons being as visible as spoons, all attempts to measure their size in the intervening decades have met with failure. What we can say is this: if an electron *does* have any size, it's less than one millionth of a trillionth of a meter, or 10^{-18} meters. We're talking *small*.

For the sake of argument, let's suppose the electron does have a size, and that size is 10^{-18} meters across. What about a speck of dust? That can be very small too by our normal standards of size—about 4 millionths of a meter, or 4 microns, for the smallest specks. Based on these numbers, a dust speck is about 4 billion times the size of an electron, and Earth is about 3 billion times the size of the dust speck, or close enough to claim that the ratio is the same. We can write our result like this (with one more ratio thrown in for good measure):

The ratio of the diameter of an electron (at its largest possible size) to the diameter of a speck of dust equals . . .

the ratio of the diameter of a speck of dust to Earth's diameter equals . . .

the ratio of Earth's diameter to the distance of the nearest star.

Inside the atom

Your basic atom consists of a dense nucleus, composed of protons and—usually—neutrons, surrounded by a swarm of electrons. Astronomer Robert Jastrow suggests that if the Houston Astrodome represented the entire atom, the nucleus would be represented by a Ping-Pong ball in the center of it.

Extending the analogy, we can imagine clouds of gnats, representing electrons, flying around the ball at discrete distances. The outermost orbiting cloud of gnats (buzzing around near the roof of the Astrodome) is the outer shell of electrons, the atom's boundary. Not only are the gnats much lighter than the Ping-Pong ball, they're also much smaller. (They might not have any size at all, even though they do exist. Subatomic particles don't behave in accordance with our ideas of normalcy!)

Almost all the mass of the atom is concentrated in its tiny nucleus, with the electrons contributing virtually nothing. It's been suggested that if the atom was a book you were sending in the mail, the electrons would represent the postage stamps.

Protons, postage stamps, and sand

How many protons and neutrons (collectively known as nucleons) are in a postage stamp? That's easy, just divide the weight of one by the other (ignoring the lighter electrons). It turns out to be about 10^{22}, a simple number to handle now that we've got some analogies to work with. Let's use the sand analogy. At 10 million grains per cubic foot, there are as many protons and neutrons in a postage stamp as there are grains of sand in a layer spread 12 foot deep across the entire continental United States (Fig. 1-2).

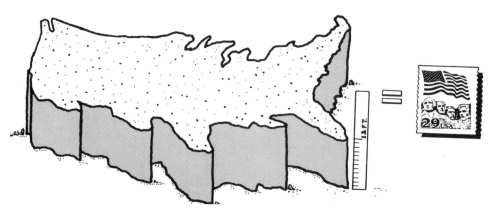

1-2 Illustrating the proton's minute size. The number of protons in a postage stamp roughly equals the number of grains in a 12 foot deep layer of sand laid across the entire contiguous United States.

Think of that next time you lick a stamp to mail a letter. By the way, that number, 10^{22}, is also the total number of stars in the visible universe (give or take a couple).

Protons, neutrons, and electrons are the basic stuff of atoms and therefore of all matter (other than short-lived "exotic" particles, which we needn't worry about here.) Atoms themselves vary greatly in size. An atom of uranium is vast compared to an atom of hydrogen. Yet all are minuscule compared to the world of our unaided senses.

Here's one last exercise to get a gut feeling for the very small, this time by visualizing carbon atoms, important constituents in the chemistry of life. Pull out a hair from your head and look at it. No less than 50,000 carbon atoms could fit end to end across the width of that thin hair of yours.

By now you should have a feel for some of the very smallest particles that make up the universe. Next we'll go to something very large, but still manageable in our day-to-day terms: the scale of our cosmic neighborhood, the solar system.

The orange and the sun

To describe the evolutions in the dance of these gods, their juxtapositions and their advances, to tell which came into line and which in opposition, to describe all this without visual models, would be labor spent in vain.

Plato, Timaeus

"You can't teach an introductory astronomy course without an orange," I said to my class. I admit some teachers portray the sun as a grapefruit, and one I know uses a basketball, but the principle is the same: a model is the best way to convey the true scale of our place in space. While it's easy enough to talk sizes and distances on paper, to truly appreciate the awesome scale involved, most people need 3-dimensional objects to actually touch and move around.

In this model, by representing the sun as a four-inch orange, everything is scaled down by a factor of some 13 billion. (This is a major shrink job, not to be undertaken lightly. If *you* were scaled down by 13 billion, you'd be smaller than an atom.)

First, you need to get an orange—or something else round—a little more than four inches across. At this 13-billionth scale, Earth is conveniently represented by the ball of a medium ballpoint pen. Your next task is well worth the destruction of a Bic. Ready?

Extract the ball from the pen using wire cutters or a pair of pliers. (Cut the very tip of the pen, just short of the ball, holding it over a bowl so the tiny ball doesn't disappear in the process.) Clean it and set the ball-Earth in your palm with the orange-sun beside it. Look at them and marvel at the disparity in sizes. (Again, if you've been reading without doing, I urge you to actually do this. Something about having the two objects actually sitting side by side in your palm makes the analogy real.) You could fit nearly 1 1/2 million Earths into the sun.

Remind yourself that the tiny ball in your palm represents that same Earth outside your window. Remember how enormous our planet appeared, with no apparent curvature, the last time you stared out at the countryside from a hilltop or out to sea from a cliff? That tiny ball represents an Earth so huge, compared to the scale of our everyday experience, that it's less than 500 years—20 generations—since it was first circumnavigated.

Now think of how small the sun seems to us, the same apparent size as the full moon. It's easy to see, from the difference in size between the ball and the orange, that the sun must be very far away. How far? That's part two of the exercise.

Going for the angst

Go outside, preferably to a park or somewhere where there's plenty of open space. Put the orange down on a rock or bench and take 13 steps away from it (38 feet, if you want to be more precise). Look back. At this scale, you're seeing the sun from Earth. Now walk around the sun counterclockwise, holding the little ball from your Bic, and imagine it's Earth in its lonely year-long orbit around the sun. Try to isolate the orange and the ball from their surroundings, imagining that they are alone in the emptiness of space.

Not quite alone, though. Between Earth and the sun, two planets also orbit: Earth-size Venus and smaller Mercury. Also we shouldn't forget our companion in orbit about the sun, the moon. Its diameter is one quarter Earth's, and at this scale it's 1¼ inches away.

Beyond Earth orbit the other planets: Mars, Jupiter, Saturn, Uranus, Neptune, and Pluto. Jupiter and Saturn are huge compared with the rest, about the size of peas and 200 and 400 feet respectively from the sun at this scale. Pluto at its greatest distance (it varies) is three city blocks away.

That's it! That's your basic solar system, reduced by a factor of 13 billion: an orange, a couple of peas, and seven even smaller objects, about 60 known moons, many dust-size asteroids, comets and the like, scattered across a few city blocks. If you can isolate these various components from their mundane surroundings, you can get a sense of how empty and how lonely we and our companion planets are in space.

After a brief bout of existentialist angst, consider where the next orange might be. At this scale, in which the solar system could easily be fitted into New York's Central Park, how far away is the closest star? A mile? One hundred miles? Rarely does anyone in my classes come close to the true answer of 2,000 miles, the distance between New York and Salt Lake City (Fig. 1-3). Imagine a few little specks of matter, none bigger than a pea, orbiting an orange in Central Park, then imagine virtual emptiness until you get to Salt Lake City. (No wonder Sartre was so glum.)

This is a far cry from those phony pictures of the solar system we all probably saw on the walls of our schoolrooms, where the planets were huge balls that practically bumped into each other as they orbited a sun, depicted only slightly larger than themselves. By creating a true-to-scale model like the one described below, you can glimpse just how lonely space is.

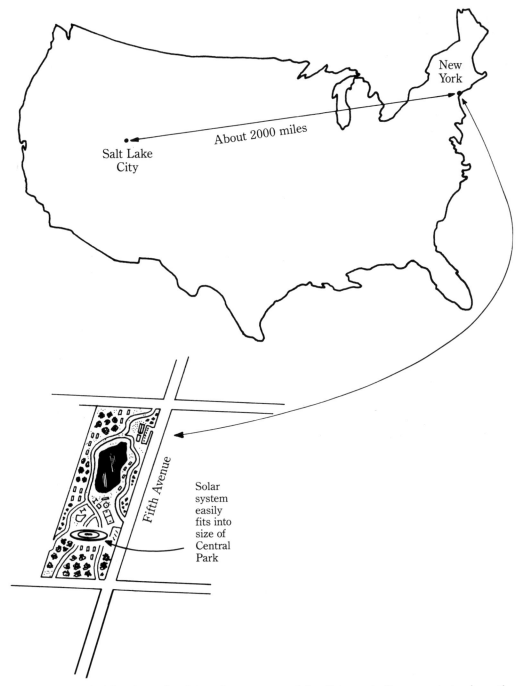

1-3 Getting a feel for the scale of the solar system and the distance to the nearest star from the sun. If the sun were the size of an orange, the next star would be in Salt Lake City.

A scale model of the solar system

Stars shine, planets are round, bridges remain geologically rather small, cells divide rapidly, atoms randomly vibrate, electrons disobey Newton, all because of scale.

Philip and Phylis Morrison, *Powers of Ten*

If you want to make a complete model of the solar system, these are the approximate measurements, working at our 13-billionth scale:

Object	Size, inches	Equivalent to	Distance from sun (average)
Sun	4.2	Orange	
Planets			
Mercury	0.015	Grain of sand	15 feet
Venus	0.037	Medium ball (of a pen)	27 feet
Earth	0.038	Medium ball (of a pen)	38 feet
Moon	0.010	Grain of sand	1¼ inches from Earth
Mars	0.020	Fine ball (of a pen)	58 feet
Jupiter	0.431	Pea	196 feet
Saturn	0.362	Pea	359 feet
Uranus	0.154	Ball bearing	724 feet
Neptune	0.147	Ball bearing	1,130 feet
Pluto	0.007	Grain of sand	1,500 feet
Nearby stars			
Alpha Centauri A*	4.7	Large grapefruit	1,970 miles
Sirius**	7.1	Small balloon	3,940 miles

*The nearest star to the sun is Proxima Centauri, 4.22 light years away. It is the smallest member of a triple star system collectively named Alpha Centauri. Alpha Centauri A, 4.35 light years away, is the largest of the three. (You can only see the system from the southern hemisphere.)

**Sirius is the brightest star in the night sky, 8.7 light years away.

One pair of eyes: from small to large

The largest structures of nature appear to be inextricably linked to the very smallest.

John Barrow and Joseph Silk, *The Left Hand of Creation*

Photo by author

1-4 The greatest distance an unaided pair of eyes can see. The fuzzy elliptical blob is the Andromeda Galaxy, M31, 2¼ million light years away. When we see it, we see light that left there over 2 million years ago. I took this photo from Glacier Point, Yosemite, a couple of weeks before forest fires resulted in the park's closure in August 1990. The streaks are airplanes, while the odd shape on the right is Half Dome, which is blurred as the telescope-mounted camera tracked the moving stars. See C-1 for what it looks like "up close."

It's easy to talk about atoms and galaxies and even to put numbers on their sizes, but what range of scales can we actually be aware of unaided, without using instruments such as microscopes or telescopes? Obviously we can see objects the size of the human body, and we can perceive objects that range up and down somewhat from that size. So we can see an ant, one thousandth our size, and a mountain, thousands of times bigger than us. Beyond that, what can we see? A human hair or speck of dust? A distant planet or star? Or can we do better than that?

The greatest distance

The greatest distance of which we can be aware, without instruments, is a very distant object indeed, the Andromeda Galaxy, known to astronomers as M31 (Figs. 1-4 and C-1). It's over two million light years away and is almost a twin to our own Milky Way.

Have you seen it? If not, I urge you to make the effort to identify this remarkable object for yourself (Fig. 1-5). Granted, it's not much to see with the naked eye—a fuzzy patch of light at best, whose presence you might need to confirm through binoculars—but, for northern hemisphere dwellers, it's unique. (Southern hemispherites also can see the Magellanic Clouds, two small neighboring galaxies to our own).

It's not just that M31 is further away than any star we can see in the sky, it's *much* further. The most distant star visible to the unaided eye is about 20,000 light years away, and M31 is over a hundred times that. In order to grasp the relative

1-5   How to find the Andromeda Galaxy, M31. The most convenient time to look for it is on a fall evening. First locate Cassiopeia, the big "W" in the sky on the far side of the Pole Star from the Big Dipper, Ursa Major. Then find the Great Square of Pegasus, beyond Cassiopeia. Now use the chart to find M31. You'll need to be away from city lights on a dark, preferably moonless night. M31 looks like a faint luminous cloud, barely visible until your eyes have adjusted to the dark. Try looking slightly off to one side of it to see it more clearly.

distances when I look at it, I imagine that stars in my field of vision—which are actually in our own galaxy—are raindrops on a windowpane and that the luminescent cloud of M31 is out there, way, way beyond the glass.

The smallest distance

The smallest distance of which we can be directly aware is more subtle. In their book and television series *The Ring of Truth*, Philip and Phylis Morrison asked, how close to atomic size can we perceive with our unaided senses? Their imaginative response was to place a very small quantity of olive oil—a quarter teaspoon—on the surface of a pond. As it spread, the film of oil could easily be seen calming the otherwise rippled water. At its limit, the film reached quite an appreciable area, some two thousand square feet. A simple calculation shows that its thickness—rather, thinness—is a mere five-millionth (0.0000002) of an inch, the size of a single molecule of oil.

If we were to start off with the depth of that film of oil and multiply it by ten, then multiply *that* by 10, then *that* by 10, and so on . . . how many times would we have to repeat the process until we arrived at the distance to M31? Let's do it in stages: if we do this multiplication process 8 times, we get to human baby size (that is, $0.0000002 \times 108 = 20$ inches); another 9 times and we've passed the moon ($0.0000002 \times 1017 = 316,000$ miles, approximately). In all, it takes a total of about 30 multiplications by 10 of the thickness of our original film of oil to reach M31!

What an impressive range of sizes—30 powers of ten, from the molecular to the galactic—that we can appreciate with nothing more than a pair of unaided eyes connected to a three-pound brain.

Timewalk

A rose-red city 'half as old as Time'!
Dean Burgon, *Petra*

Time is what you read from a clock.
Albert Einstein

Our universe had a beginning. This statement, with which the majority of astronomers would agree, is all the more astonishing when you consider the presumption involved, to claim to know the seemingly unknowable. Our certainty derives from vast amounts of data coming from different lines of inquiry, all of which seem to point to a genesis some 15 billion years ago. The exact age is not so important as the idea itself. A universe with a finite age? Is this more surprising than an eternally old universe? It's like asking which is more curious: a man without a navel (implying no forebears), or a man of infinite age?

An aged, as opposed to an ageless, universe means that time has a limit, and that limit is 15 billion years, give or take a few billion years (which cosmologists are apt to do rather freely). That's how long ago it was when the (misnamed) Big Bang occurred, the moment when space, time, and everything began. Let's assume 15 billion is the correct figure. Similar to the orange-ball experiment, this next exercise is designed to awaken in you an awe at how tiny we are and how large the universe is. Before it was distance. Now time is the dimension we're trying to grasp.

Start with a piece of paper, for instance this page you are reading. It's about one two-hundredth of an inch thick. We're going to visualize time as a length, to let this thickness represent the length of time of 30,000 years. Why 30,000? Because the oldest known human-made object that seems to have been meant to last dates from about then. It's known as the Venus of Willendorf, (Germany)—a ceramic statue of a woman's torso.

We need to start with something as thin as a sheet of paper because these last 30,000 years are almost nothing compared to the age of the universe. At this scale, our solar system formed 64 feet ago, and the Big Bang happened about 200 feet ago. Here's the exercise: on a blank sheet of paper, write the word *NOW* in big letters. Go outside and pin the paper to a wall, so that the word faces the wall. Pace out 200 feet (about 65 steps) and mark the spot, which will represent the moment of the Big Bang (Fig. 1-6). The distance between the Big Bang and NOW represents the long corridor of time, all of time, every second that has ever passed.

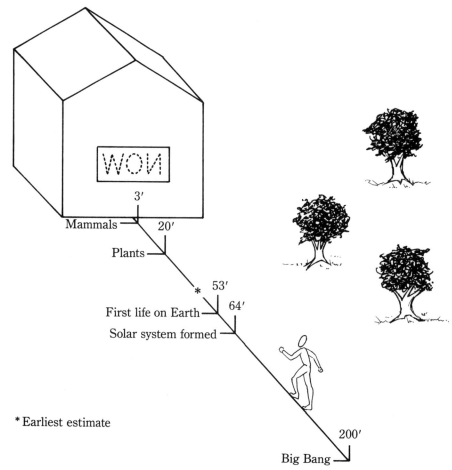

1-6 A walk through time. If 200 feet represents the entire age of the universe, the thickness of a sheet of paper represents everyone you've ever heard of, all of history. The present, NOW, is on the far side of the paper.

Back to the present

Start walking towards NOW. Every foot of your journey represents 75 million years. Every inch is a little more than six million years.

A little more than two thirds along your journey (64 feet from NOW), our home galaxy, the Milky Way, formed and our sun—one of multitudes—"switched on" as the fires of nuclear fusion began to convert hydrogen to helium deep within its core. At the same time, the sun's planets were accreting out of cosmic gas and dust.

Another few paces and the crust of our planet cooled and soon after (between 3.5 and 4 billion years ago), the miracle happened: life first appeared on Earth. Tenuous and hesitant at first, it was to evolve into the millions of species that share the surface of the planet today.

About 40 feet from NOW, the moon was finished with ejecting the molten lava, which created the lunar *maria* ("seas"). From now on, it's geologically dead.

Twenty feet from NOW, the first plants formed. Just 14 feet from the present, nature happened upon a wonderful invention that was to vastly accelerate the pace of biological evolution: sex. At 5 feet (400 million years ago), our ancestors migrated from the seas to dry land. Three feet from NOW, hard on the heels of dinosaurs, our mammalian forefathers entered the scene. The dinosaurs lasted until 65 million years ago, 10 inches from NOW.

At 9 inches, horses appeared; 6 inches, cats and dogs; 4 inches, grass; 2 inches, Antarctica started to freeze. A little less than one inch from NOW on our compressed time scale (about 5 million years ago), we split off from the chimpanzee line of evolution, and a million or so years later, our ancestors (the best known of whom is Lucy), first began to walk upright. At the same time, the first continental sheets of ice began to form, and they've been waxing and waning ever since. (We're now in an *interglacial period*, waiting for the next advance.)

We're getting down at last to the thickness of your sheet of paper, the last 30,000 years of time. Put your hand on it. On the side you're touching, our Neanderthal cousins were disappearing, leaving ours as the only species of hominid to spread around the world. On the other side (facing the wall) lies the present, NOW. Incredibly, in the very thickness of this paper lies history, or in Carl Sagan's words, "every person we've ever heard of . . . all those kings and battles, migrations and inventions, wars and love, everything in the history books . . ." All of it is right here, between the front and back of a single sheet of paper.

As you feel it between your fingers, look back at your Big Bang marker and wonder at the age of the universe and everything that ever was.

Gravity 101

It is enough that gravity really exists and suffices to explain the phenomena of the heavens and the tides.

Isaac Newton, about 1684, justifying the "outrageous" concept of forces acting at a distance.

We are constantly surrounded and invaded by invisible forces and particles. Some examples:

- A battery-powered transistor radio has no material connection to anything other than the table on which it sits. You can pick it up and turn it around, yet it still plays, responding to the invisible waves of the radio station it is tuned to. Those waves are part of the electromagnetic spectrum.

- The compass responds to lines of magnetic force. How does the needle know which way to point, even when it's in apparently empty space?

- Every second, hundreds of millions of massless (we think) particles called neutrinos stream through our bodies. We don't feel them, but they're as real as the pages of this book. They come from the sun, lacking any electric charge, and just zip on through us. Earth is no barrier to them, so at night as many pass through us from below (after travelling right through our planet) as they do in the daytime when they come from the sun overhead.

This leads us to gravity—the invisible force that rules the motions of planets around suns, suns around the centers of galaxies, and the relative motions of galaxies and clusters of galaxies. Whereas a radio can detect radio waves, and a compass can detect magnetism, on Earth you need no intermediary device to detect gravity. Your own sensations do it for you. (I suppose you also could use your radio to detect gravity. Lift it up and let it go, watching very carefully. Kids: Don't try this at home!)

Noticing gravity

Stop reading for a minute, close your eyes and be aware of gravity's inexorable clutch, pulling you down to the center of Earth (Fig. 1-7). What would it be like if gravity was stronger or weaker, or even if it disappeared altogether? Isn't it odd that we normally don't notice gravity, which governs every movement we make? It's ubiquitous in space and time, yet we need to be reminded that it's there. Why aren't we more aware of it?

An analogy with sound might help us understand. Like gravity, sound waves are invisible, yet we're constantly made conscious of them. A baby's cry, a dog's bark, the car horn brings instant recognition and often an instant response. All these are examples of sudden, distinct, intermittent sounds. What about constant, monotonous sounds? If you live near a freeway, do you hear the cars? If you work at

1-7   Gravity in action: How the ancients might have imagined what it was like living on the "underside" of Earth. This meteor-hunting scientist is in Antarctica, demonstrating just how hard it is to hang on Down Under.

a computer, do you hear the cooling fan? The refrigerator compressor motor? Your partner's breathing in bed? The sound of the sea or the wind? Normally, we're only aware of intermittent or unusual sounds. When a sound is a constant background accompaniment, we don't notice it. Similarly, gravity is a constant background companion in our lives.

Weight or mass?

What do you weigh? Between 100 and 200 pounds? Let's look at what those numbers means. On the moon, you'll weigh a fraction of what you weigh here, so weight is a variable depending on where you are. Your mass, however, is the amount of matter in your body, approximately equivalent to the number of nucleons you contain, irrespective of where you are.

Your weight is the force you feel right now, pulling you towards Earth's center. It depends on three factors: your mass (the more mass you have, the more you're pulled down), Earth's mass (on the moon, you'd weigh about one-sixth of what you weigh here, so a 180 pound astronaut weighs 30 pounds), and your distance from the center of Earth (about 4,000 miles). If you were in space at twice that distance, 8,000 miles from Earth's center, you'd weigh one quarter of what you weigh now. At 12,000 miles from the center, you'd weigh one ninth of what you weigh now.

These three factors are the parameters of a famous equation Isaac Newton claimed to have discovered when he was only 23 years old. (He didn't publish the results until over 20 years later, in 1687, when Edmund Halley, of comet fame, paid for publication.) Newton formalized the relationship between the three factors by saying this: *The force between you and Earth (your weight) is proportional to your mass times Earth's mass divided by the square of the distance between the centers of the two masses.*

This applies to more than you and Earth. It works between an apple and Earth, the moon and Earth (see *Gravity: Newton vs. Einstein*), Jupiter and the sun, or two galaxies thousands of light years apart. This is Newton's *universal* law of gravitation.

Did Newton actually believe in this odd concept of an invisible force acting at a distance? The quotation at the start of this essay sounds rather defensive, and indeed, there's evidence that he knew he'd only found a temporary solution. For instance, he also wrote, ". . . I desired you would not ascribe innate gravity to me. That gravity should be innate, inherent, and essential to matter, so that one body may act upon another, at a distance through a vacuum . . . is to me . . . an absurdity . . ."

What an insight it was, temporary or not! Newton's simple but powerful law took thousands of years to figure out, from Aristotle in ancient Greece to Kepler and Galileo in the early 1600s. It revolutionized astronomy with its simple and universal mechanism, which explained celestial motions: by measuring how fast an apple falls, we can predict the motion of distant galaxies.

Halley summed it up when he ranked Newton's discovery as one of the four "greatest achievements of mankind," along with the establishment of a social community, agriculture, and (could you have guessed?) wine making.

Gravity: Newton vs. Einstein

Having thereby compared the force required to keep the moon in her orb with the force of gravity at the surface of the Earth, [I] found them to answer pretty nearly.

Isaac Newton, about 1684.

Gravity rules the universe. We know of only four basic forces: gravity, electromagnetism, and the strong and weak nuclear forces. Of these four (and we have good reason to believe there are no more), gravity alone has the ability to cause one mass to significantly affect another mass millions of light years away. Of the other three forces, the strong and the weak are essentially limited to subatomic scales, while the third, electromagnetism, has a small effective range. (Why? Because anything larger than subatomic size contains approximately the same number of positively and negatively charged particles, which cancel each other out, resulting in a net force of zero.)

Although gravity dominates the solar system and the cosmos as a whole, it's by far the weakest of the four forces. Compare it, for instance, with the electromagnetic force by picking up a nail with a one-ounce magnet. Here's Earth, 200 trillion trillion times more massive than the magnet, yet the magnet's electromagnetism easily outpulls Earth's gravity!

Isaac Newton achieved a great synthesis of scientific knowledge when he demonstrated that the force on an apple as it falls to Earth is the same force that causes the moon to fall Earthwards. The reason the moon stays in orbit, he said, is because two opposing forces balance out. One comes from the moon's tangential velocity (Fig. 1-8), which wants to move it away from Earth. The other is its gravitational attraction to Earth. The moon orbits at just the right distance from us so these forces balance out. (If it travelled slower, it would orbit closer to Earth, and vice versa.) The fact that this balancing act works just as well with a long and narrow elliptical orbit as with a circular one allowed Newton's peer, Edmund Halley, to compute the elongated orbit of the comet that was named after him.

Almost perfect

Newton's basic formula, which allows us to compute the force of gravity acting between two objects from their masses and distance apart, is used to plot the course of space vehicles. It allowed NASA's mission planners to estimate the location of Voyager 2 to within a few *feet* after its four-billion mile trip to Neptune. Newton's understanding of gravity was almost perfect.

Almost, but not quite. It took Einstein—another synthesizer of knowledge—to explain gravity by, essentially, dispensing with it (Fig. 1-9). He introduced the idea that there's no such thing as empty space, even when there are no material objects nearby. All of space, he said, possesses the intrinsic property of curvature, which you can think of as an invisible web, or grid, permeating everywhere. Instead of Newton's gravity, which causes two bodies to attract each other as if there were some invisible elastic thread between them, bodies move in Einstein's universe in

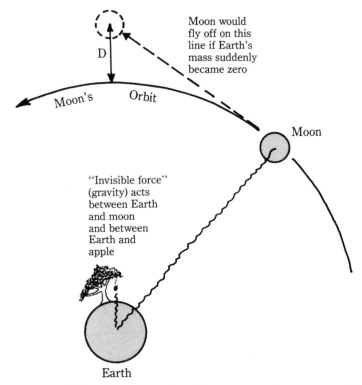

D

Moon would
fly off on this
line if Earth's
mass suddenly
became zero

Moon's   Orbit

Moon

"Invisible force"
(gravity) acts
between Earth
and moon
and between
Earth and
apple

Earth

1-8 Newton's Gravity: If Earth's mass suddenly became zero, the moon would fly off along
the broken line, and in one second would be a distance D from its normal orbit. But
Earth's gravity "pulls" it towards Earth the same distance D in one second, so the
moon remains in orbit. Newton imagined gravity as an invisible force between any two
bodies. For the apple and Earth, that force is proportional to: (mass of apple) times
(mass of Earth) divided by (square of the distance between their centers of mass). The
apple tugs at the Earth while the Earth tugs at the apple. Because the apple is so comparatively light, it does (nearly) all the moving. The moon's tug on Earth is more
noticeable, so much so that it's chiefly responsible for ocean tides.

response to their local curvature. We can thus dispense with the notion of forces
acting at a distance, which made Newton so uncomfortable.

Imagine letting go of a marble on the side of a bowl. The marble doesn't
"know" what the overall shape of the bowl is or what's pulling it towards the center. All it "knows" is that the little patch of bowl on which it's sitting is sloping
down, and it rolls in the direction of that slope. Similarly, the falling apple and the
orbiting moon do not "know" that Earth exists. In our picture of the universe
according to Einstein (Fig. 1-10), the only thing they're "aware" of is the invisible
curvature of their immediate surroundings, and it is that to which they respond.

Try this: drop a pen. Your pen doesn't somehow sense that 4,000 miles away
lies the center of Earth, tugging at it. All it knows and responds to is its immediate
surroundings in space. As it happens, that space is curved, causing it to fall.

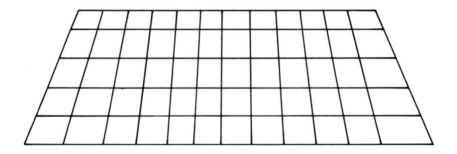

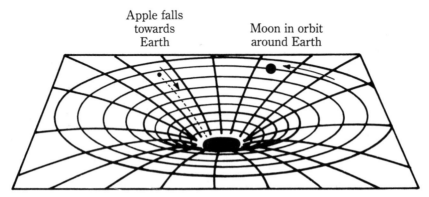

Apple falls
towards
Earth

Moon in orbit
around Earth

1-9 Einstein's Gravity: Above, an "embedding diagram" symbolizing space
with zero curvature, far from any mass. Below, an embedding diagram
showing space curved by Earth's mass. Neither the apple nor the moon
are "aware" of Earth's presence. All they "know" is the curvature of their
local space, which is affected by adjacent space, which is affected by its
local space . . . which is eventually affected by Earth's mass.

Why is space *curved* in the first place? Because of the presence of mass. No
mass, no curvature. The mass of Earth—or the sun, or anything—tells space how
to curve. Picture how space is curved by Earth. One way we can visualize this is
with embedding diagrams like those in Fig. 1-9.

In the top of the figure, we see that even "empty" space is filled with an invisible web of curvature. Even though the curvature is zero, as indicated by the
straight lines, it's still an intrinsic property of space.

The bottom figure attempts to show what it's like near a massive body, in this
case, Earth. The apple falls "down" towards the center of Earth, while the moon
orbits Earth like a marble spinning around the inside of a bowl. You can think of
the second diagram as showing a frictionless rubber sheet with a baseball in the
middle. Each portion of the sheet is distorted, not by the ball, but by the rubber
that surrounds it, which in turn is distorted by the rubber that surrounds *it*. All the
way back to the baseball, or Earth.

In a phrase: Space tells mass how to move, and mass tells space how to curve.

Archives, California Institute of Technology

1-10 One man's fight against gravity: Einstein at CalTech. (The inertia of the spinning wheels prevents the bike from falling over.)

2

The sun, our local atomic power station

He who goes forth shining.
Translation of "Tonatiuh," Aztec name for the sun.

Our local star, the sun, is central to our lives and to the solar system as a whole. Almost the entire mass of the solar system is concentrated in that central fiery ball. Around it orbit the nine planets, their moons, and countless asteroids and comets. All are affected, to a greater or lesser degree, by the sun. For example, most of the energy that powers life on Earth comes from sunlight. Consequently the sun rules our climate, photosynthesis, and a host of other phenomena that dominate our day-to-day and year-to-year existence. In addition, the rhythms of our lives are ordered by two natural sun-dependent cycles: the 24-hour night-and-day cycle; and the annual seasonal cycle, as the hemisphere on which we live tilts towards or away from the sun.

In this section, we'll examine six broad aspects of the sun: what it looks like (including a discussion of sunspots); how it works (starting with mankind's unraveling of the structure of the atom); the parallels between nuclear fusion on Earth (the hydrogen bomb) and fusion in the sun; the ultimate fate of the sun; how fusion in massive stars produced the elements of our bodies; and how energy from the heart of the sun lets us see, for instance, a leaf.

What does the story of the atom and the atomic bomb have to do with the solar system? Everything. In order to understand the sun—what it is, how it works, what its future is—you need to understand the atom. The sun's tremendous power derives from harvesting atomic energy in a process known as thermonuclear fusion. It's a process that has only been revealed to us in the last hundred years, linking as it does the very small with the very large. Our present knowledge has come with far-reaching and, for some, fatal consequences, because the sun's mechanism is the same mechanism that empowers hydrogen bombs. As we'll see, the story of understanding the sun is the story of inventing the Bomb.

Meet your local star

And pluck till time and times are done
The silver apples of the moon
The golden apples of the sun.

W.B. Yeats, *The Song of Wandering Aengus*

Stars come in many varieties. Of the hundreds of billions of stars in our galaxy, about one in 25 are "G-type" stars, including the sun. The G-designation refers to our star's color. Just as we can infer the temperature of a hot metal bar from its color (dull red means relatively cool and blue-white means very hot), a star's surface temperature can be read from precise measurement of its spectral color. Hot "blue" stars with designations O, B, A, and F are much more energetic than the sun and burn out faster. Most stars are K and M type, that is, they're cooler than the sun. The mnemonic, *Oh Be A Fine Girl, Kiss Me*, gives you the order from hottest to coolest.

G-type stars appear to be the best candidates to support life due to their stability and relatively high-power output. Hotter stars are less stable and cooler stars might not be energetic enough to support life on orbiting planets, assuming such planets exist. Our middle-ground star certainly works well. It has a surface temperature of about 6,000 K, which is around the boiling point of tungsten. (High temperatures are most conveniently given in K, for Kelvin, without the word *degrees*. Zero K is the coldest temperature theoretically possible, which is about minus 460 degrees Fahrenheit.) This is both hot enough to support life here on Earth and stable enough to maintain that life over a long period of evolution.

In composition, the sun is a mixture of about three parts hydrogen (the lightest element) and one part helium (the next lightest). Sixty percent of the sun's mass is in the central two percent of its volume, its core, where the temperature is an unimaginable 15 million K, and the pressure is billions of times that at the surface of Earth.

By studying the sun, we can infer much about other stars. The fact that the sun is a star wasn't always obvious, because the sun seems so different from the other stars. The sun appears in the day and the other stars are seen at night! Only in the last four hundred years have we understood that there's no intrinsic difference between them. As Newton said, "The light of the fixed stars is of the same nature as the light of the sun." The only reason the sun appears so bright is because it's so close: sunlight reaches us in eight minutes, while light from the next-closest star takes over four years.

Beyond the photosphere

We'll examine what goes on in the sun's interior later in this chapter. For now, let's consider its outer layers. When we glance at the sun, we see its photosphere, literally *ball of light*. This is the sun's visible surface, a 200-mile thick "skin," nominally quite smooth, but frequently marred by clusters of sunspots (Fig. 2-1).

Above the photosphere, the sun's atmosphere consists of the transparent *chromosphere* with the rarefied *corona* above. Because of the intensity of the photo-

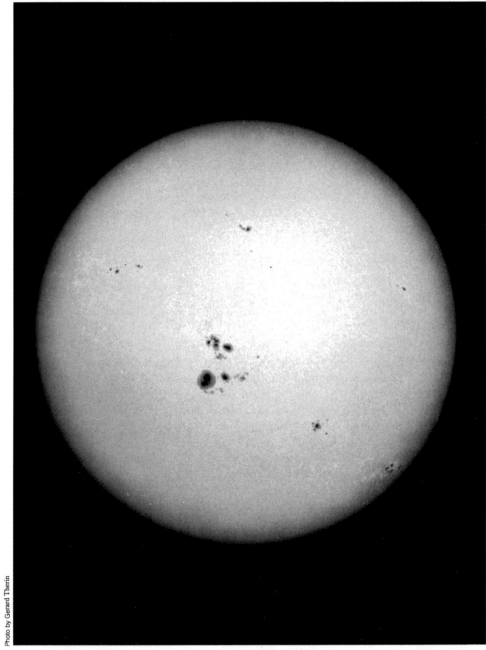

Photo by Gerard Therin

2-1　The sun's disk. When we view the sun through a telescope equipped with a safe solar filter, we see its visible surface, the photosphere. Usually we can see sunspots. Their number varies greatly, in accordance with the sun's 11-year cycle of activity. This photo was taken on February 22, 1991 near a time of maximum solar activity, as can be inferred from the unusually large number of spots. To get some idea of scale, Earth is about one quarter the size of the largest sunspot seen here.

sphere, we can't see the corona with the unaided eye, except during a total solar eclipse. There is a lot going on there, however, as anyone who's seen the white coronal wreath during such an eclipse will enthusiastically confirm. In addition, prominences, immense arches, and loops of superheated gas abound. They follow the vagaries of the sun's intense magnetic field and can last for weeks or months (Fig. 2-2).

What we can't see directly, at any time, is the solar wind. This is a veritable gale of charged particles storming out from the sun at over a million miles per hour. We can experience it indirectly, however, by observing the tails of comets that, like grasses in the wind, always point away from the sun. Coming or going, a comet's tail is caught up by the pressure of solar wind particles (and also solar radiation) heading outwards from our star.

The solar wind is responsible for the Aurora Borealis and Australis (northern and southern lights). Acting as an immense extension of the sun's magnetic field, the wind interacts with Earth's own magnetic field. Charged solar particles collide with atoms high in Earth's atmosphere near the magnetic poles: spectacular auroras result (particularly in higher latitudes), a reminder that there's more to the sun than sunlight.

Tears on the sun

Either the sun sheddeth tears or she is blemished by spots.

A Jesuit's comment on viewing the sun through a telescope, 1612.

The sun's visible disk, the photosphere, is a violent sea of gases at temperatures of 6,000 to 10,000 K. You can see its cellular granularity in the detailed photograph of the sun's disk (Fig. 2-3), together with those evil-looking pock-marks, sunspots.

The existence of sunspots was a controversial subject until the invention of the telescope in 1608. In keeping with the contemporary belief that the heavens were divine and therefore perfect, Aristotle taught that the sun was unblemished. The astonishment of the Jesuit quoted above echoed that of Galileo, who had noted sunspots through his telescope only a couple of years earlier. Yet records of sunspots had been maintained by other cultures for centuries. (Sunspots are visible through haze, but looking into the sun is reckless to the eyes. *Don't try it!*) In 300 B.C., the Greek Theophrastus said he saw blotches on the sun, while Chinese astronomers recorded over 100 sunspots between 28 B.C. and 1638 A.D., according to historian Robert Temple. *A Life of Charlemagne*, written in about 807 A.D., has a clear reference to them.

With the telescope, astronomers had a rigorous tool to observe sunspots on a day-to-day basis. Over 300 years ago, the sun's uneven rate of rotation—27 days at the equator, over 32 days near the poles—was inferred from the motion of sunspots marching across the face of the sun. In 1843, an alert amateur astronomer, Heinrich Schwabe, realized that their number increased and decreased in an 11-year cycle. We now know that the sunspot cycle corresponds to other sun-related activities, such as prominences (Fig. 2-2), as well as auroras and disruption of radio communication on Earth.

Photo by Gérard Therin

2-2 Solar prominence, an immense cloud of gas reaching up some ten Earth diameters from the sun's surface into its chromosphere. (Over 100 Earths would fit across the diameter of the sun.) This 1989 photograph was taken with a coronagraph, an instrument invented by a French astronomer in 1930 to artificially eclipse the disk of the photosphere, whose light would otherwise drown out any prominences. Compare with C-2.

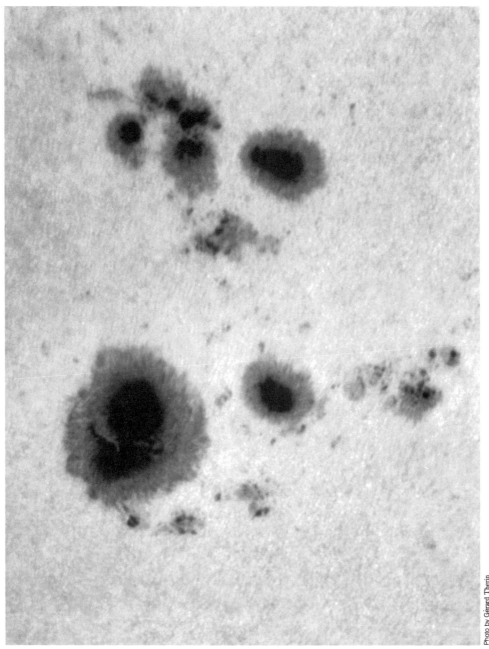

Photo by Gérard Therin

2-3 Sunspot detail. At three times the magnification of Fig. 2-1, and with an additional filter to bring out detail, we see delicate radial lines in the penumbral areas of the sunspots surrounding the darker umbra. You can think of sunspots as the "doors" through which powerful lines of magnetic force loop in and out of the photosphere. Notice also the granularity of the surrounding photosphere. Each "granule" is a huge cell of hot gas.

Fortunately, you don't need a telescope to see sunspots. Welder's glass #14 or solar filters (sold by the thousands for the 1991 eclipse) will shield your eyes from harmful radiation, and you'll be able to see large ones directly or smaller ones with a filter taped securely over the objectives of a pair of binoculars.

What are they?

Sunspots are the visible manifestations of intense loops of magnetic force fields that pierce the photosphere. We see them as patches of gas, which only appear dark because they're cooler (perhaps by 1,000 K) than the surrounding photosphere (Figs. 2-1 and 2-3).

It's now generally believed that at the start of an 11-year cycle, the sun's magnetic field is calm and organized, with lines of force running quietly from pole to pole just like on Earth. At that time, few sunspots are seen. After a year or so, the lines start to get "stretched" because of the sun's uneven rate of rotation.

Eventually they become raveled, like an untidy invisible ball of stellar wool. The visible result, which builds up to a maximum after $5^1/_2$ years, is a profusion of sunspots—locations where these knotted lines of intense magnetic force pass through the photosphere. One of nature's self-healing miracles then happens: the "knots" become so tight that they break, and the lines rejoin, now knot-free. After a further $5^1/_2$ years, things are once again calm and serene, and the number of sunspots is at a minimum. In the process, the sun's magnetic field is reversed, and it takes a further 11 years of knotting and healing to bring the sun back to where it started, for a complete cycle of 22 years.

Counting sunspots is a fine long-term experiment. If you keep track of their numbers over the months and years, you'll be able to observe the regularity of our star's 11 year/22 year sunspot cycle, as Heinrich Schwabe did.

What makes sunshine?

Let the hot sun
Shine on, shine on.

W.H. Auden, *Look, Stranger!*

What mechanism makes it possible for stars like our sun to shine over a period of billions of years without any external source of energy? When astronomers and philosophers of old tried to figure this out, they imagined actual fires in the sky, because fire was the only way they knew in which light could be created. (Stars were a separate problem from the sun, because only in the last few hundred years was it realized that the sun was a star.)

Thales, founder of the Ionian school of philosophy in Greece in the seventh century B.C., claimed that Earth lay at the center of the universe enclosed by a huge perforated brass sphere. Outside the sphere, an eternal fire raged, visible only through the holes. Each star was simply a hole in the sphere. Absurd as the specifics sound to us, Thales was one of the first to understand the crucial concept of a *model*, in which the remote is compared with the familiar.

The question wasn't really taken up again until the last century, spurred on by a problem set by what was then the comparatively new science of geology, the understanding of Earth itself. According to geologists, our planet was not thousands of years old, as interpreted from the Bible, nor 20 to 100 million, as most physicists then believed; it was at least a billion years old. (We now know the age of Earth to be about 4.5 billion years.)

A billion year-old Earth presented two separate problems: one, why was Earth still so warm, when it "should" have lost most of its original internal heat; and two, how could the sun keep producing energy for that long?

The first problem was solved in 1896 with French Physicist Antoine Becquerel's discovery of *radioactivity*, the spontaneous emission of energy by certain elements. This led to the realization that Earth's internal heat was constantly being renewed by radioactive decay of elements, such as uranium, deep inside our planet.

In trying to answer the second problem, nineteenth century physicists looked first to coal, then meteor collisions, then gravitational collapse as possible mechanisms to power the sun. Finally they realized that the second problem was allied to the first: Both involved processes in which energy was released from the previously uncharted atom.

We now know that the sun and other stars shine by the conversion of their mass into energy, in a process called thermonuclear fusion. Understanding came slowly, and it wasn't until 1938, with the work of German-born American physicist Hans Bethe, that the inner workings of stars were solved.

At about the same time, scientists realized they could do the same thing here on Earth, as we'll see.

The atom: Source of the sun's energy

I was brought up to look at the atom as a nice hard fellow, red or grey in color, according to taste.

Ernest Rutherford, physicist (1871-1937)

To really understand the sun and the other stars, we need to know something about how they work and where their energy comes from. For that, we have to delve into the world of the very small, the atomic world, because the sun's energy, which makes you and me possible, comes from the transformation of atoms.

The atom

In Greece 2,400 years ago, two philosophers, Leucippus and Democritus of Abdera, made an inspired guess. They said that all matter was made up of atoms, literally "those which can't be cut." Despite the fact that there was no way then to check it out, some people believed them. The debate in those days was whether atoms actually had any weight or not. It would take over two thousand years to prove that their guess was essentially right.

In 1808, English scientist John Dalton revived the Atomists' concept when he suggested that elementary substances—elements—were indeed composed of atoms. His novel contribution was to propose that there isn't just one type of atom.

In a stroke of genius, he proposed that each element is composed of its own distinctive atoms. As we'll see, an element's properties depend on the unique composition of its atoms and, in particular, the number of protons it contains.

The word *element* implies that we're dealing with something that can't be further simplified. For many years after Dalton's breakthrough, it was thought impossible for one element to be changed (or transmuted) into another, because the atoms of which elements were composed were utterly fundamental. That changed in 1897 when J.J. Thomson, working in Cambridge, England, published research on something he called the *negative corpuscle*—the electron, which showed that atoms carried individual negative electric charges. Because atoms were neutrally charged, the implication was that they could be "cut" into at least positive and negative particles.

In a classic experiment a few years later, New Zealander Ernest Rutherford aimed a stream of alpha particles (atoms of helium minus their electrons) at a very thin sheet of gold foil. While most passed through the foil with little change in direction, some were bounced back. It was, he said, "almost as incredible as if you fired a 15-inch shell at a piece of tissue paper and it came back and hit you!" His explanation for this extraordinary observation was that a few of the alpha particles were hitting a central atomic core. Suddenly the atom wasn't a homogeneous "plum pudding" made up of positive and negative particles scattered evenly about. Now it was seen to have a structure, comprising a dense core, or nucleus (which we now know to be composed of both positively-charged protons and neutral neutrons), surrounded by Thomson's orbiting negatively-charged electrons. It was the tiny nucleus from which a few of Rutherford's alpha particles were bouncing.

We've already encountered Robert Jastrow's analogy of the atom (*The size of the atom*), in which a Ping-Pong ball in the center of the Astrodome represents the proton and neutron-filled nucleus. Gnats flying around the stadium, as far away as the roof, represent swarms of electrons, with nothing in between. That wall, this book, you, and me are nothing but a huge cloud of atoms made up of mostly empty space. (Physics is nothing if not humbling.)

With the discovery of neutrons in 1932, scientists had a handle on the three regular building blocks of atoms: protons, electrons, and neutrons. They also had a pretty good idea of what an atom looks like and what holds it together. Also, and in keeping with Dalton's idea, they knew that the chemical characteristics of each element depend on the number of protons in each of its atoms. That number, the atomic number, varies from one (hydrogen with just one proton) to 92 (for the heaviest naturally-occurring element, uranium, each of whose atoms contains 92 protons) and beyond for artificially-produced elements.

Understanding atomic structure led to the realization of the alchemists' dream of converting one element into another. If it was possible to add protons to, or subtract protons from, the nucleus, could elements be transmuted? And if that were possible, could energy be spontaneously created in the process?

Radioactivity

The key to answering these questions lay in Becquerel's radioactivity, by which process the nuclei of atoms decay or disintegrate by spontaneous emission of particles called alpha, beta, and gamma rays. Following its discovery, radioactivity was investigated in the early years of this century by Pierre and Marie Curie, winning for them and Becquerel the 1903 Nobel Prize for Physics. (Eight years later, Marie Curie was awarded a second Nobel Prize, this time for Chemistry.)

Marie Curie's curiosity led to her becoming one of the first victims of cell-destroying radioactivity. As she lay dying of leukemia in January 1934, her daughter and son-in-law, Irène and Frédéric Joliet-Curie, showed her evidence that radioactive energy could be generated artificially, in their laboratory. Ernest Rutherford had demonstrated 15 years earlier that one atom could be changed to another, by bombarding nitrogen with alpha rays. Now the Joliet-Curies proved that energy could be *spontaneously* generated in the atomic transmutation process.

This was the practical outcome of Albert Einstein's 1905 discovery, that it should be possible to create energy by the destruction of mass (see the following section on bringing the sun's energy to Earth).

The husband and wife team were awarded the Nobel Prize for their work. In their acceptance speech, Frédéric noted the relevance of the discovery in relation to the mechanism that powers stars. After discussing normal stars, he went on to say, ". . . a star invisible to the naked eye may become very brilliant and visible without any telescope—the appearance of a nova. This sudden flaring up of the star is perhaps due to transmutations of an explosive character like those which our wandering imagination is perceiving now . . ." Change *nova* to *supernova*—a cataclysmic explosion of a dying massive star following its rapid collapse—and his guess was right on, as would be shown by astronomers studying the evolution of stars.

However, bringing the energy of the stars to Earth proved to be the more immediate quest, and one that was to change the course of history.

Bringing the sun's energy to Earth

A new thing had just been born; a new control; a new understanding of man, which man had acquired over nature.

> **Isidor Rabi, physicist, after detonation of the first atomic bomb, July 16, 1945.**

$E = mc^2$

This well-known equation, key to the sun's energy, ushered in a new era of first physics and later world politics. Within months of publication of his Special Theory of Relativity in 1905, Albert Einstein published a three-page paper in which he showed that a corollary of his new theory was that a body's mass was a measure of its energy content. His equation tells us that a very small quantity of mass is equivalent to a great deal of energy, because the c^2 part of the equation (the velocity of light squared) is a very large number indeed. (For instance, light can travel the equivalent of seven times around the equator in one second.) Think of it this way: mass is concentrated energy.

Radioactivity was the mechanism that could put Einstein's equation into action, and once the genie was out of the bottle, it didn't take long for that to happen. A mere 11 years elapsed between the Joliet-Curies' creation of energy by spontaneous transmutation of elements, to the first atomic bomb in 1945. The world, as noted elsewhere, has been sadder and wiser ever since. The real crunch (literally) came a few years later, with mankind's emulation, in the hydrogen bomb, of the sun's source of power, thermonuclear fusion.

The atomic bomb

Let's first define a couple of terms. An element can be transmuted, or changed, to another by altering the number of protons in its nucleus either by fission or fusion. *Fission* is the splitting of the nuclei ("splitting the atom"), here applied to heavy elements like uranium and plutonium. *Fusion* is the uniting of nuclei of light elements like hydrogen and helium. The important thing to remember is this: both fission and fusion reactions sometimes produce less total mass than the mass you started with. In that case, the "missing mass" shows up as energy.

Back to the atomic bomb. The last few years of work leading to its creation took place in secrecy during the World War II, under the name of the Manhattan Project. At 0530 hours, July 16, 1945 the first bomb, code-named *Trinity*, was detonated in the desert at Alamagordo, New Mexico.

Three weeks later, on August 6, the 4-ton "Little Boy" atomic bomb was dropped on the southern Japanese city of Hiroshima. In that explosion, a mass of about four pounds of uranium was fissioned, causing it to lose about one thousandth of its mass in the process. That's not much—about what a single page of this book weighs—but, being equivalent to 12,500 tons of TNT, it was enough to level ninety percent of the city.

The early nuclear bombs were uranium and plutonium *fission* bombs. However, a much more efficient method of extracting energy from the atom is through the fusion of certain types of hydrogen. This was achieved for the first time in a fiery explosion (*Mike*) on November 1, 1952, in which the Eniwetok island atoll in the Pacific was obliterated. This type of weapon is usually called an H-bomb (for hydrogen) or, more clinically, a thermonuclear device.

The Mike test used a 10 megaton bomb (that is, it had the power of 10 million tons of TNT), so it was about 800 times more powerful than the Hiroshima bomb. In the explosion, a mere three pounds of matter—about what three books like this weigh— were converted into energy. For an H-bomb to achieve the necessary pressure and temperature for fusion to occur, the fusion material is surrounded by a blanket of fissionable material. So a fission bomb sets off the fusion bomb—and typically *that* sets off a secondary fission reaction. The whole unholy affair is called a fission-fusion-fission device.

Today, nuclear power stations, using the fission reaction of uranium fuel, supply about sixteen percent of the world's electricity. The dream for decades has been to achieve a controlled *fusion* reaction to generate electrical power. With seawater providing the fuel and virtually "clean" waste, the promise is enticing—especially when you consider how little material is actually consumed. If all the water in your next bath was converted into energy, it would supply the entire needs of the United States for two weeks. Immense technical and engineering problems are involved, and to date (and, in my opinion, for the foreseeable future) we're not going to be able to do it.

Yet fusion is an ongoing fact of life for the sun and other stars. Let's see how they achieve it.

Journey to the center of the sun

Till the sun grows cold,
And the stars are old,
And the leaves of the Judgment Book unfold.

Bayard Taylor, *Bedouin Song*

All our Earthly efforts at transforming matter into energy are puny in comparison to what goes on at the heart of the sun. There, every second, 5 million tons of matter are converted by thermonuclear fusion into energy, a fraction of which nourishes life on this planet. In the very heart of the sun, hydrogen atomic nuclei are squeezed to immense pressures and temperatures, causing them to fuse. In the most common mechanism (the proton-proton chain reaction), four nuclei of hydrogen are converted into one helium nucleus, a few lighter particles, and energy in the form of gamma and X-rays (Fig. 2-4).

To do this on Earth in an H-bomb, we have to use the explosive power of a fission "blanket" wrapped around the material to be fused in order to achieve the necessary pressure. Inside the sun, gravity does the job. Imagine lying down on the ground with a slab of sidewalk on top of you. Now imagine another slab being added on the first. Now another . . . soon you'll be squashed. The same thing is happening at the heart of the sun, where the gravitational pressure of all the outer layers squeezes the inner core so tightly that fusion occurs.

The process has been occurring naturally and continuously for about 5 billion years, when the sun first condensed out of a cloud of interstellar dust and gas. The process defines a star: when sufficient mass accretes, nuclear fusion results and a star is born. A mass equivalent to 80 Jupiters is sufficient, and anything having more mass is automatically a star. The sun, for instance, has a mass of just over 1,000 Jupiters. (In theory, there is an intermediate stage: *brown dwarfs* are wannabe stars. Containing between 10 and 80 Jupiter masses, they undergo a brief period of nuclear fusion in their lifetimes. Curiously, none have been found to date.)

Our sun currently uses hydrogen as its fuel to create thermonuclear energy. Five billion years from now, it will start to use the helium ash for fuel. More massive stars also use other elements for fuel, going through several stages of fusion,

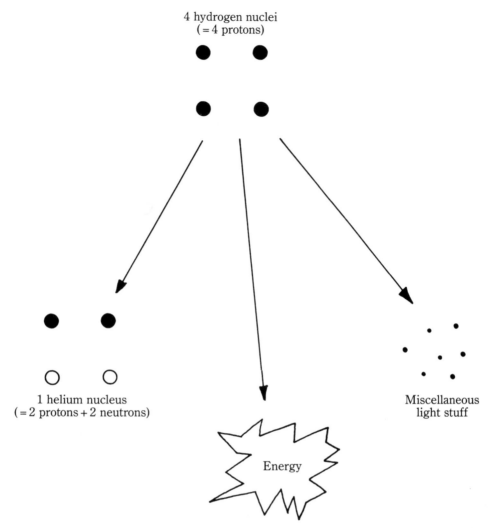

2-4 Energy from the sun. The sun, now halfway through its lifetime, has been producing energy for nearly 5 billion years. It does so by converting hydrogen to helium, in the process "losing" five million tons of mass every second. The mass is converted to energy, and this diagram illustrates the most common reaction taking place in the heart of the sun, the "proton-proton" reaction. The nuclei of four hydrogen atoms are converted by nucleosynthesis into a single nucleus of helium-4, miscellaneous light particles, and energy.

to produce progressively heavier elements, including carbon, oxygen, magnesium, neon, silicon, sulfur, and iron.

The once and future sun

The nuclei of hundreds of millions of tons of hydrogen are fused into helium nuclei every second in the heart of the sun. In the process, 5 million tons of mass is lost, converted (according to Einstein's $E = mc^2$) into a prodigious amount of energy: nearly a billion billion billion watts. Earth only receives 2 billionths of the total, but that's plenty to keep life alive and well here, nearly 100 million miles away.

A loss of 5 million tons a second sounds pretty phenomenal. At that rate, the Great Pyramid of Giza would be gobbled up in a second, but the sun, 300,000 times more massive than Earth, has plenty of staying power.

For 5 billion years, the sun's hydrogen fuel has been generating energy that we perceive directly as sunlight. The process generates an enormous pressure pushing out from the core, counteracting the gravitational pressure pushing in. That's why the sun hasn't collapsed on itself under its own weight—yet. The equilibrium between these two gargantuan forces will be maintained so long as sufficient hydrogen is available.

In another 5 billion years, the core hydrogen will be so depleted that gravity will briefly win the battle, resulting in a gigantic increase in density—and thus temperature. When the core temperature reaches about 100 million K (compared to the present 15 million) the helium ash at the core will begin to fuse. In the process, the density of the shell of material surrounding the core will also increase, enabling previously unconverted hydrogen there to also fuse.

The result will be a wild inflationary period as our sun grows to a monstrous size, expanding beyond the orbit of Venus, perhaps reaching—and certainly incinerating—Earth in the process. During this expansion, the sun's surface temperature will drop, and any aliens out there would see its color change from yellow-white to the cooler orange of a red giant star. This temporary swan song, as the sun fends off death, will last for another 100 million years, as long as the helium lasts. After that, it will shrink into a white dwarf.

Not all stars die in such a relatively gentle process. Fortunately for us, more massive stars go through particularly violent death throes. That's what makes it possible for us to be here, as you can read in the next section.

Our bodies, our stars

Mankind is made of star-stuff.

Harlow Shapley, astronomer (1885-1971)

We owe our corporeal existence to events that took place billions of years ago, in stars that lived and died long before the solar system came into being.

Robert Jastrow, astronomer (1925-)

The fact that I'm writing, and you're reading, this essay tells us something about the universe. The heavy elements in our bodies—present in skin, blood, bones, teeth—weren't around in the early universe, before stars formed. The only stuff around then was hydrogen and helium, in roughly a three-to-one combination, with a smattering of other light elements. (We still find approximately the same mix in the sun.) So where did the other elements that make up us—oxygen and iron in our blood, calcium in our bones, nitrogen in our proteins, and all the rest—come from?

From stars more massive than our sun. From stars massive enough to create, in their dying moments, the conditions necessary for the creation of such elements. Our own sun is a typical enough star, yet in its lifetime of 10 billion years, it can synthesize only a couple of elements: helium from hydrogen (as it's now doing) and carbon from helium (as it will do towards the end of its active life, 5 billion years from now).

In order to synthesize elements heavier than carbon, you need stars that are at least 40% more massive than the sun. That extra mass translates to unbelievable temperatures—over 300 million K—in the last stages of a star's life. That's how hot it has to be for nuclei of carbon atoms to fuse, creating heavier elements like oxygen. A massive star goes through stages of synthesizing and burning ever more massive elements beyond carbon, until it reaches iron.

Iron is a unique element. The protons and neutrons in its nucleus are packed so tightly that no energy can be extracted from it. Yet we know—by looking at ourselves and the earth beneath our feet—that heavier elements such as silver, gold, lead, and uranium abound. Where did they come from?

They were created in the very final moments in the life of a massive star, when the essentially inert iron in its core could offer no resistance to the crushing gravitational pressure of surrounding material and in the unimaginably violent explosions that immediately followed. We call such explosions *supernovae*. The famous supernova of 1572, observed by Tycho Brahe, was as bright as Venus, while in 1987 the first supernova visible to the naked eye since the telescope's invention was spotted in the Large Magellanic Cloud (a satellite galaxy to our own, visible only from the southern hemisphere).

Much later, the remains of these exploded stars coalesced under gravity's orders to form new stars and, in at least one instance, planets. On one of those planets, life happened— eventually to ask the question, "Where did the stuff of our bodies come from?"

Sunlight, from there to here

The sun is coming down to earth, and the fields and the waters shout to him golden shouts.

George Meredith, *The Ordeal of Richard Feverel*

Glance outside at some green foliage. A journey that began tens of thousands of years ago was just completed—in the retina of your eye.

Almost all sunlight is emitted from the top of the photosphere, the 200-mile-thick skin of the sun. How does the energy generated in thermonuclear fusion at the sun's core get to the photosphere? Very slowly! Although the direct distance is only about 400,000 miles, it takes tens of thousands of years for energy from the core to reach the photosphere surface, thence to escape as sunlight. Let's follow the history of sunlight, from its creation in the heart of the sun to the retina of your eye.

From the sun's core to the photosphere

The photons that just smashed into your retina originated in the heart of the sun, at a minimum of about 50,000 years ago, when Neanderthals roamed the forests of

Europe. Energy from the furnace of nuclear fusion was then released in the form of high-energy gamma rays, highly energetic photons with very short wavelengths. Each could travel only about half an inch at a time before colliding with an atom. The result changed the atom's energy level, and typically two or more photons were emitted at lower energy levels.

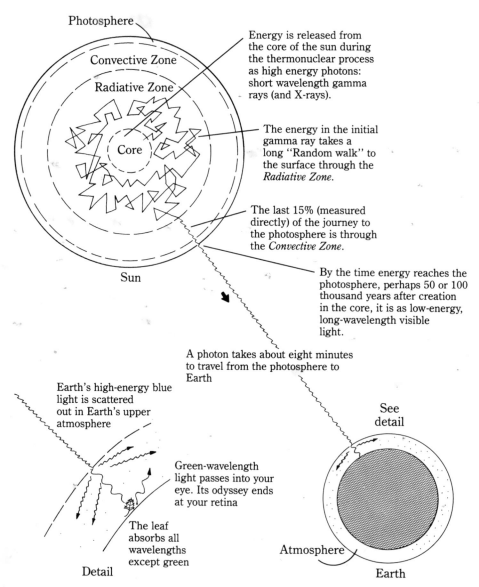

Photosphere

Convective Zone

Radiative Zone

Core

Sun

Energy is released from the core of the sun during the thermonuclear process as high energy photons: short wavelength gamma rays (and X-rays).

The energy in the initial gamma ray takes a long "Random walk" to the surface through the *Radiative Zone.*

The last 15% (measured directly) of the journey to the photosphere is through the *Convective Zone.*

By the time energy reaches the photosphere, perhaps 50 or 100 thousand years after creation in the core, it is as low-energy, long-wavelength visible light.

A photon takes about eight minutes to travel from the photosphere to Earth

Earth's high-energy blue light is scattered out in Earth's upper atmosphere

Green-wavelength light passes into your eye. Its odyssey ends at your retina

The leaf absorbs all wavelengths except green

See detail

Atmosphere

Detail

Earth

2-5   A long odyssey for the energy of a photon, from the core of the sun to the retina of your eye. It can take from 50 thousand to as long as 20 million years for nuclear-produced solar energy to travel from the center of the sun to its surface, thence to Earth in another eight minutes.

This process of absorption and re-emission, usually with the production of new photons, can be likened to a 50,000 year-plus drunken walk. Photons randomly bounced around in the sun's radiative zone (see Fig. 2-5), constantly changing direction—and multiplying—from one collision to another. Physicists call such movement *Brownian motion* after nineteenth century botanist Robert Brown, who first noticed this random-motion phenomenon while observing plant spores floating in water.

Eventually, after countless encounters, which terminate in a comparatively brief and straightforward convection cycle, the photons reached the sun's surface, the photosphere. By this time, about eight minutes ago, they were much less energetic than when they had started out, having degraded from gamma rays to rays of visible light. Collectively, the photons were now what we refer to as *sunlight*.

From the photosphere to your eye

A photon (a little package of light) travels at 186,000 miles per second in the near-vacuum of space. We're about 93 million miles from the sun, so (using an unexpected numerical ratio) we can see that it took them 500 seconds, or about eight minutes, to get from there to here.

As the photons zipped through Earth's atmosphere, the more energetic of them—the blue wavelengths—collided with dust and water vapor, and in this way were scattered across the sky. It's the scattered blue light from the sun that makes our sky appear blue. (See *Blue skies and red sunrises*.) If Earth had no atmosphere, the sky would appear jet black, just as it does to astronauts in orbit.

Getting closer to home now, our photons hit the foliage outside your window. Instantly, most were absorbed by pigments in the leaves. Which ones? Those having wavelengths of blue, yellow, and red—everything except green, which was bounced off, or reflected. That's why leaves appear green. When we speak of a leaf or a wall or a book as green, we actually mean that it absorbs all wavelengths *except* green.

As waves of green photons entered your eye, still travelling at nearly 186,000 miles per second, they were refracted, or bent, by various layers of transparent goop that makes up your eye: cornea, aqueous humor, lens, and finally vitreous humor. The refraction serves to focus light to a point just in front of your retina.

So far, that's the easy part. What happened next is both more complicated and less understood. At the end of their epic journey, our photons had their energy converted into electrical energy in your multilayered retina, sending signals through your optic nerve deep into your brain, which interpreted the messages in such a way that you registered "green leaves." Don't ask me how: even neurologists have trouble understanding it.

3
Earth and moon

I see a great round wonder rolling through space . . .
Walt Whitman, *Salut au Monde!*

This section examines one rocky planet and its moon. The planet is one of nine orbiting a stable, relatively hot star located near the edge of a spiral arm of a great galaxy of stars, the Milky Way. We call the planet Earth.

Earth is beneath our feet and, as atmosphere, over our heads. Our lives take place at the surface of this rocky ball. We barely acknowledge its three-dimensional depth, for other than a few comparatively shallow shafts and wells, we've not touched the inside of our planet. We live out our lives where solid rock meets gaseous air and sometimes, wading at the edge of the sea, where solid and gas meet liquid water.

Here at the surface, we live in the zone of maximum gravity. Rising above Earth's surface or burrowing deep inside our planet has the same effect—we lose weight. We weigh the most right here at the surface. (Actually, we weigh the most at the North or South Pole, where a person who weighs 200 pounds at the equator weighs 201 pounds. But that's another story.)

The moon's influence on life on Earth is secondary to the sun's; however, life would be very different without it—perhaps nonexistent. The moon's most visible effect on life is its daily contribution to ocean tides. Although the sun, our local star, is very massive, its tidal influence is less than the moon's, because it is 400 times further away. Acting together, moon and sun cause the monthly tidal cycles, which also affect life, both large and small. In addition to tides, the moon reflects sunlight, which illuminates Earth's night side. This silvery beam was more important in days of old, before artificial lighting became common, especially on full-mooned nights when our ancestors could see to hunt, dance, and make mischief.

Like many moons, ours is locked by tidal friction into *synchronous rotation* (see Glossary) with Earth, so it rotates on its axis in the same period it takes to orbit its parent planet. As a result, we always see the same face (Moon Maps 1 and 2), and a photo of the far side is simultaneously surprising and familiar (Fig. 3-1).

NASA

3-1 Part of the far side of the moon. Tidal friction over billions of years has locked the moon's spin into one-to-one resonance with its orbit around Earth, so we always see the same face. This image shows much of the side we never see from Earth. It's centered on Mare Orientale, a 600-mile diameter impact basin as large as Texas on the moon's western limb. (The moon's near side is on the right of the photograph: the huge dark area, upper left, is Oceanus Procellarum, and the circular dark area on the right, just below the center, is Mare Humorum.) The dark area in the center of the basin is lava which welled up from the moon's interior over 3 billion years ago. Orientale is the youngest and best preserved of the large lunar impact basins. The photo was taken on December 9, 1990 by the Galileo spacecraft on its long and complicated (once past Venus, twice past Earth) trip to Jupiter.

You'll find a potpourri of notions about Earth and the moon in this section. We'll look at the origin of the moon, new ways of seeing Earth, Earth's orbit, and what makes the sky blue. In addition, we'll marvel at the singular phenomenon that links three bodies (sun, moon, and Earth) in one of nature's most spectacular events: a total eclipse of the sun.

Our place in space

. . . like lying on one's back as we did in Spain when we slept out looking up between the fig-branches into the star-corridors, the great seas and oceans of stars. Knowing what it was to be in the universe.

John Fowles, *The Collector*

Our planet, with us and the stuff of our daily lives on its surface, is remote in space, unspeakably small and lonely in the context of the sun and its retinue of planets. Yet with all our present knowledge, with our satellite photos and instant global weather maps and other extensions to our senses, we are, for the most part, less conscious of our place in space than were our forebears a few generations back. Now, when most of us venture out at night, street and auto lights mute our view of the planets and stars. Two hundred years ago, no such impediments sullied our views of the night skies, and I imagine that most people then could have unhesitatingly pointed out Saturn, Sirius, or Sagittarius.

Four exercises

Here are four simple exercises to consciously cultivate a visceral sense of our place in space:

- Look at the full moon though binoculars for five or ten minutes of concentrated viewing. After a while, you'll start to see it as a sphere, not as the flat disk it normally appears to be. Remind yourself that you're also standing on a sphere.

- Watch the sun set into the sea or behind distant hills. As it sinks out of sight, concentrate on locking the sun into place. Feel you and Earth beneath your feet revolving slowly away from the sun.

- Using binoculars, lose yourself in the night sky. Lie on your back and stare long and intently, moving slowly from one star to another. You'll soon experience the illusion of being out there, not anchored to Earth but freely floating between the stars—best done on a summer's night far from city lights.

- About noon, face west and close your eyes. If you're in the northern hemisphere, you're now looking through the front windscreen of spaceship Earth, in the direction it moves around the sun. Count up to five slowly. In that five-second interval, you've moved 100 miles on the solar-orbit freeway around the sun, travelling at about 70,000 mph.

There's really no substitute for getting away from Earth and looking back, like the astronauts who went to the moon did. Perhaps two hundred years hence, lunar trips will be as easy as flying to Hawaii. Meanwhile, get out the binocs!

Moon musings

The moon is nothing
But a circumambulating aphrodisiac

Divinely subsidized to provoke the world
Into a rising birth-rate.

Christopher Fry, *The Lady's Not For Burning*

The moon as our ever-present companion in space is graphically illustrated in Fig. 3-2. Just one quarter of a million miles away, it's the distance a well-maintained car might be driven in its lifetime. If you drove at a steady 55 mph, it would take you six months to get there. A radio signal from the moon, travelling at the speed of light, takes a scant 1¼ seconds to reach us.

NASA

3-2   Earth and moon together: the only image to date of Earth and its moon in a single frame. It was taken on September 18, 1977, by Voyager 1, 13 days after launch as it headed towards its 1979 rendezvous with Jupiter. You can see eastern Asia, the western Pacific Ocean and part of the Arctic. The photo is a composite from three images taken through red, green and orange filters. Earth is much brighter than the moon, so the moon has been artificially brightened by a factor of five. At this distance, about 7 million miles, Earth and moon are at true scale relative to each other. Compare with Fig. 3-3.

I remember listening to Neil Armstrong and Buzz Aldrin during the first manned moon landing in July 1969. Their conversations with Mission Control in Houston had a languid quality, with odd pauses between question and answer. They heard Houston $1^1/4$ seconds after we did, and it took another $1^1/4$ seconds for us to hear them after they spoke. The $2^1/2$ second pauses are usually edited out of the historical documentaries I've seen broadcast on TV. That's too bad—the pauses *are* the history.

Dethroning Earth

In 1543, Nicholas Copernicus published his book, *Concerning the Revolution of Celestial Spheres*, in which he argued persuasively for a new order—instead of the sun and planets orbiting Earth, as had been taught for over 1,500 years, he said it was the sun around which all the planets revolved. Not only had Earth been dethroned from the center of the universe, now it was just another planet.

Yet, we on Earth were still special. Wasn't it true that those other planets had no moon, but ours did? Enter Galileo with his telescope.

In his 1610 book, *The Starry Messenger*, Galileo reported on his humbling observations. He claimed to have spied not one, but four moons in orbit around the planet Jupiter (they're known today as the Galilean moons), effectively stripping Earthlings of their claim to uniqueness. First it was Copernicus demoting Earth from its central throne, then Galileo, claiming that other planets also had moons. It was quite a come-down.

Today we know that seven of the nine planets in the solar system have moons, ranging from our one to Saturn's seventeen (at least). Yet our moon *is* special. It's easily the largest moon in the solar system relative to its parent planet (excluding Pluto and its moon Charon, which are literally oddballs by any measure). If you looked at Earth from afar, you wouldn't think of it as being alone in space. You would see Earth as the larger member of a duo, four times the diameter of the other (Fig. 3-3). Compare that, for instance, to the largest moon in the solar system, Titan, which has just one twentieth the diameter of its parent planet, Saturn.

The bathtub ring of life

When the moon is roughly overhead or underfoot (i.e., on the opposite side of Earth to overhead), high tides occur, and when the moon is off to one side, we experience low tides. The complete cycle—high, low, high, low and back to high—takes about 25 hours, the period Earth takes to spin beneath the moon. (It would be 24 hours if the moon was stationary, but it revolves around us, of course.) Because of its influence on ocean tides, some researchers believe the moon might have played a critical role in the genesis of life on Earth.

The whole question of how life started on Earth is far from resolved. Did life originate in warm tidal pools on the edge of an ocean full of nutrients? Did hot springs provide the nurseries for sulphur-metabolized precursors of regular, DNA-based life? Were organic clays the birthplace of our ancestors? Or did life arrive ready-made on comets from far away?

We don't know. We don't even know what life is. Even if we had all the compo-

Stephen P. Mezaros and the Astronomical Society of the Pacific

MOON

EARTH

3-3 Sizes of Earth and the moon compared. At this scale, the moon would be ten feet away from Earth.

nents for a microorganism lined up in a row, we couldn't make a living creature from them. It's a far cry from amino acids, which we do know how to create in the laboratory, to a living, self-replicating organism.

Having said that, let's look at one scenario (out of many) that attempts to explain how life arose on Earth. This particular model is interesting from an astronomical point of view, because it requires our healthy-sized moon to cause large and regular tides. The tidal range would have been greater 4 billion years ago, when the moon was closer to Earth than it is now, and the sun's contribution to tidal forces (currently about one third) was much less.

In this model, life originated in tidepools on the shoreline of some ancient ocean, where uncountable combinations and permutations of atoms and molecules resulted in the formation of polypeptides, amino acids, and other building blocks of DNA. Countless comets fell to Earth, each one bringing a new supply of interesting, volatile material. Earth's early atmosphere—rich with carbon dioxide, ammonia and methane, host to a zillion chemistry experiments under the unfiltered ultraviolet light of the sun—turned the ocean into a consommé of organic chemicals. (It's been likened to chicken bouillon; it's also possible that it was too dilute for the scenario outlined here to work. Many unknowns make it difficult for us to know for sure.)

According to this model, tides were responsible for the necessary concentration of life-forming stuff. Each high tide added fresh and fecund flotsam to the shoreline, and the beaches became a vast bathtub ring of potential life, literal hotbeds of chemistry. Eventually a prototype DNA or RNA molecule, with the ability to self-reproduce, emerged from the chaos. Perhaps, as some researchers now believe, this happened several times before a continuous chain was established. The rest is nearly 4 billion years of evolutionary history.

Moon-gazing

As you watch the moon slowly changing from one phase to another through your binoculars, you will begin to realize, perhaps for the first time, that this is another world with a ragged, irregular surface on which a truly incredible amount of detail can be distinguished. Indeed, you may become discouraged at first because there is so much detail visible on the moon's surface.

Alan E. Nourse, **The Backyard Astronomer**

The moon is so convenient. At least a hundred times closer to us than the next closest major celestial bodies (Venus and Mars), the moon is a handy way-station for future explorations of the solar system and beyond, and a perfect site for telescopes of all kinds. It's astonishing that no one has set foot on the moon since December, 1972, when astronaut Gene Cernan became the last of our kind to walk there.

While waiting for the next lunar mission to get underway, you still can explore the lunar surface with nothing more sophisticated than a pair of binoculars strapped onto a photographic tripod. With this simple apparatus, you'll be able to follow the moon through a complete series of lunar phases, as new features are revealed night after night (see *Binoculars and the moon*).

Despite the romantic associations, the full moon isn't necessarily the best time to observe the moon, for the same reason that a camera-mounted flash doesn't create a very interesting photograph of you: your face looks flat and lacks depth (it's called pancake lighting). Moving the light source to one side creates shadows that give the subject depth and bring out details, whether we're talking about a floodlight to one side of your face or the sun to one side of the moon's face.

Moon Maps 1 and 2 (see Appendix) give you the best of both worlds, with detailed photographs of both the full and a composite of the quarter and three-quarter moon. By using these photos with the keys, you'll be able to identify most major lunar features.

The man in the moon

The most obvious characteristic of the moon, one we're aware of with the naked eye, is that it comes in two basic colors: dark gray and light gray. In the dark gray areas, we see the eyes and other features of the "Man in the moon." These are the level *maria*, which cover about one sixth of the moon's surface. The light gray areas are the moon's mountainous highlands.

The maria, "seas" in Latin, were at one time thought to be oceans of liquid water. It was a good guess. For over half a billion years liquid lava (magma) poured from the moon's still-hot interior into enormous impact-created basins. The highland regions were untouched by this volcanic activity and, other than "fresh" craters, look much as they did soon after the moon was formed about 4½ billion years ago.

That outpouring of lava is ancient history. For the last 3 billion years, the moon has been essentially a dead body. With surface gravity only one sixth (and a mass one eighteenth) that of Earth, it has neither sufficient gravity to retain an atmosphere (and so allow erosion), nor a large enough internal heat source to create crustal movements. Thus, the meteorite record for billions of years is a perfectly-preserved record book, easily read from Earth by you and me.

While viewing with binoculars isn't quite the same thing as walking on its surface or driving near Mare Serenitatis, as astronaut David Scott did (Fig. 3-4), you'll still be able to visit it and Clavius (Fig. 3-5), site of the U.S. moonbase in *2001: A Space Odyssey*, and a thousand other lunar features in your imagination.

3-4 Apollo 15 commander David Scott and the Lunar Roving Vehicle (LRV) at the edge of Hadley Rille near the western edge of Mare Serenitatis.

Where did the moon come from?

All explanations for the origin of the moon are improbable.

Harold Urey, American chemist and Nobel Laureate (1893-1981)

Over twenty years after Neil Armstrong planted his right boot on the surface of the moon, making his ". . . one giant leap for mankind," planetary scientists are still

Photograph by Gérard Therin

3-5   Clavius crater, site of the U.S. moonbase in 2001: A Space Odyssey.

arguing about the moon's origin. The debate, which has raged for centuries, was given impetus by souvenirs from the astronauts' visit: moon-stuff. In all, the six Apollo landings yielded 843 pounds of lunar material, ranging in size from dust to basketball-sized lumps. Laboratory analysis of all this brought the question of the moon's origin into the limelight again.

Historically, three main hypotheses have been proposed (Fig. 3-6):

- The Simultaneous Creation or "Sister" Hypothesis: In this scenario, Earth and moon formed side by side in space, drawing on the same material. Instead of coalescing into one body, two bodies emerged, one orbiting the other. The problem with this is, if they had come from the same source, you would expect them to be more similar overall than they actually are. Earth is rich in iron (mostly in its core) and water. The moon has very little iron and no water.

- The Fission, or "Mitosis" Hypothesis: Charles Darwin's son, astronomer George H. Darwin, promoted this one. He realized that the distance between Earth and the moon is increasing (due to tidal friction), so our satellite must once have been much closer to us. His idea was that the early, molten Earth spun so fast it bulged at the equator, then elongated into a bowling pin-shaped object. The small end snapped off and became the moon. Requiring an extraordinary rate of spin, and thus an unfeasible angular momentum (see Glossary), it sounds about as unlikely as the mathematics tell us it is.

- The Capture Hypothesis: This holds that a passing extraterrestrial body was captured by Earth into orbit as it cruised by. (Twenty liberating years ago, it was dubbed the Pick-up Hypothesis.) This sounds like it might work, but again the mathematics show it to be an extraordinarily unlikely, zillion-to-one chance. You've got to have the object in just the right place with just the right relative velocity; otherwise it either escapes or crashes into Earth.

There's another problem with the Capture Hypothesis. Although, as we've just seen, the moon's overall composition is unlike Earth's, it is remarkably similar to Earth's crust and mantle (the rocky part) if you ignore volatile materials like water and nitrogen. The similarity appears to be too great if the two bodies had completely distinct origins.

Giant collisions

Each of the above theories has severe drawbacks. In the mid-70s, a group of scientists re-evaluated what it was like in the early solar system. They already knew that conditions then were far removed from the neat and tidy state we see today. Even though most of the planets and their moons were happily orbiting the sun and each other, many large bodies were still orbiting the sun rather haphazardly, waiting for an accident to happen.

It appeared inevitable to the investigators that giant collisions would happen, in accordance with the generally-accepted *accretion* model of planetary formation. This says that, as the original disk of dust and gas orbited the proto-sun, dust

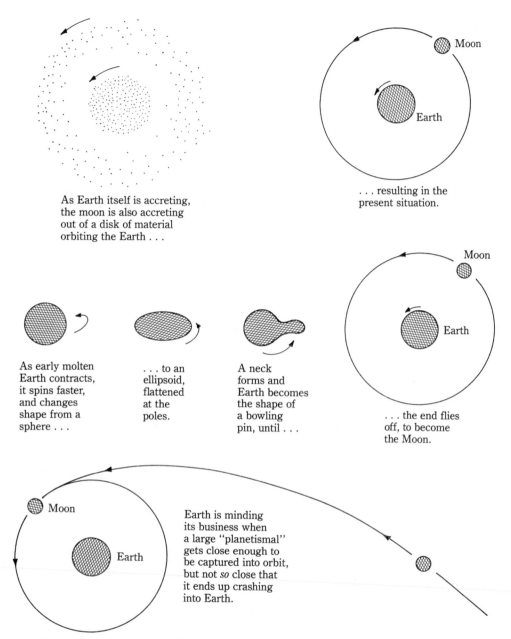

As Earth itself is accreting, the moon is also accreting out of a disk of material orbiting the Earth . . .

. . . resulting in the present situation.

As early molten Earth contracts, it spins faster, and changes shape from a sphere . . .

. . . to an ellipsoid, flattened at the poles.

A neck forms and Earth becomes the shape of a bowling pin, until . . .

. . . the end flies off, to become the Moon.

Earth is minding its business when a large "planetismal" gets close enough to be captured into orbit, but not *so* close that it ends up crashing into Earth.

3-6 Formation of the moon: Three older hypotheses. (Top) Simultaneous Creation: The moon accreting at the same time, and from the same source material, as Earth. A related hypothesis, "precipitation," had the early Earth spinning particles off into orbit, where they later accreted. But why is there no water and so little iron on the moon? (Middle) Fission: The problem here is that early Earth requires an unrealistically rapid spin rate for this to work. (Bottom) Capture: And here, too many variables have to be exactly right for a passing body to be captured in Earth's orbit. It's much more likely for it to either escape or collide with Earth.

grains collided to make stones, which collided to make rocks, which made boulders, which made bigger boulders, and so on in a hierarchy up to planet-sized objects. So the last major collisions must have been huge—large enough, perhaps, to explain several odd features of our solar system:

- Uranus spins unnaturally on its side, nearly at right angles to its orbit around the sun. Perhaps it was hit on the top or bottom by one of the last large wandering bodies.

- Similarly, the reason for Venus' backward spin might be that it too was hit, only this time on the edge spinning towards the impactor, reducing the planet's angular momentum.

- Perhaps Earth was struck near the edge spinning away from its impactor, increasing its angular momentum, thus neatly explaining the origin of the moon: the *Collision Theory*.

Mother, daughter, and dad

It worked like this: An errant Mars-sized (i.e., a body having half Earth's diameter) object struck the newly-formed and still-hot Earth a glancing blow. The object itself was destroyed (most of it ending up in Earth) while some of the material of both the collider and the collidee (Earth), heated to incandescence by the energy of the impact, was hurled into Earth-orbit. A few hundred, or perhaps thousand, years later, the material had coalesced into our moon. If you like, Mother Earth spawned her daughter, the moon, after an intimate encounter with another body (Dad) (Fig. 3-7).

This scenario could explain many unusual features of both Earth and the moon, for instance, why Earth tilts 23 degrees (giving us seasons) and why our orbit around the sun isn't a true circle (it's slightly elliptical). Best of all, it could explain why there's so little iron in the moon. Although iron is the predominant element in Earth's core, as a result of *differentiation*, comparatively little is found in the surrounding mantle. Differentiation is the process by which heavier materials migrated towards Earth's center when the planet was young and still molten. By the time the alleged impact occurred, little iron was left in the mantle, so it was iron-poor mantle material that was thrown into orbit.

Most of the heavy elements in the impacting object wouldn't have made it into orbit either. They would have fallen back to Earth in the aftermath of the collision.

The Collision Theory explains apparent anomalies in moon-rocks ferried back by Apollo astronauts. In accordance with what we've just discussed, they're deficient in iron. Also, they contain virtually no volatiles. This also fits because it implies that the moon coalesced from material so hot that any water and or other volatile material would have boiled away. Other investigators, studying the angular momentum of the Earth-moon system, have demonstrated that the mechanics of the theory are feasible providing the body was quite large, i.e., the size of Mars.

One satisfying by-product of the Collision Theory is that it incorporates elements from all three previous models: it explains the compositional similarity of the moon with Earth's outer layer (minus volatiles) in an allusion to Simultaneous

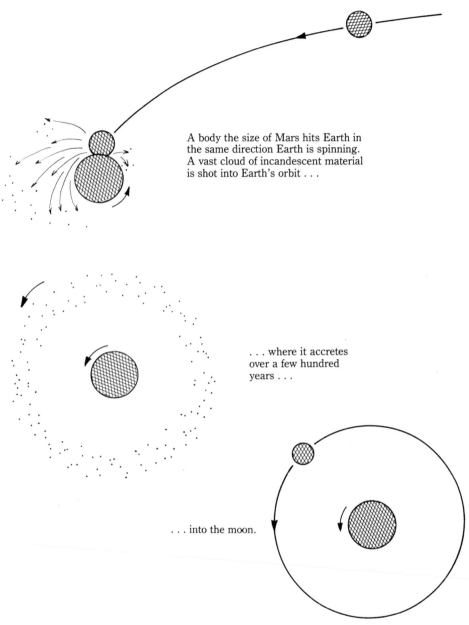

A body the size of Mars hits Earth in the same direction Earth is spinning. A vast cloud of incandescent material is shot into Earth's orbit . . .

. . . where it accretes over a few hundred years . . .

. . . into the moon.

3-7 Formation of the moon: Mother and Daughter, or Collision Theory. This scenario looks very promising in the light of analysis of moon rocks, since it explains their deficiency in iron and volatile materials, including water. If early Earth was impacted by a Mars-sized planetesimal, a massive quantity of vaporized material from both impactor and impactee would have been flung into space. Because Earth already had time to differentiate (see text), most of its iron was deep in the core, and so unaffected by the collision. The moon would have subsequently formed from the iron-deficient accretion disk. The scenario could also explain Earth's tilt and slightly elliptical orbit.

Creation; it offers a mechanism for increasing Earth's angular momentum, in a throwback to the Fission Hypothesis; and it incorporates the Capture Hypothesis' requirement for another body to be involved.

Picturing the impact

Assuming the theory is correct, what did the impact look like? After studying supercomputer simulations, one of the original researchers, astronomer William Hartmann, wrote: "The calculations show that the impactor probably struck a glancing blow, shearing off much of the mantles of primordial Earth and the impactor itself in a stupendous cloud of luminous vapor. Initially most of the iron core of the impactor traveled on, though slowed by the impact. But unable to escape Earth's gravity, it looped back to crash into the disrupted Earth, eventually merging into our planet's core. Much of the mantle debris from both bodies also crashed back into Earth. But a small fraction of the mixture stayed in orbit where it eventually coalesced to form the Moon" (*Astronomy*, June 1989).

Hartmann's reference to "luminous vapor" might be an understatement. The hot silicate gases released during the impact would have been "almost as bright as the surface of the sun." If this scenario is correct, our moon was born in a fiery catastrophe unparalleled in the history of the solar system for both its violence and its improbability.

The moon affects all life on Earth. While life might have arisen in its absence (or maybe not—see Moon musings), conditions without it would surely be very different here: it's a safe bet to say that I wouldn't be writing this book and you wouldn't be reading it if there was no moon. Here's a grateful toast to a freak collision that (probably) occurred $4^{1}/_{2}$ billion years ago.

Harvest, full and blue moons

Shine On, Harvest Moon

Jack Norworth, song title, 1908

Earth's yearly 600 million-mile circuit around the sun defines its orbital plane. It's roughly the same plane in which the other planets (other than Pluto) travel, and it's called the *ecliptic*. Like that of most planets, Earth's axis is tilted. Imagine a giant needle going through Earth from pole to pole. Instead of the needle being exactly perpendicular to the ecliptic, it's angled at about $23^{1}/_{2}$ degrees, so the North and South Poles are alternately tilted towards the sun, giving us seasons (Figs. 3-8 and C-4).

For northern hemisphere dwellers, the *summer solstice* is the moment when Earth's North Pole is maximally tilted towards the sun. As the day of the solstice approaches, the sun appears to be a little higher in the sky at noon. The solstice, literally when "the sun stands still," is the moment when it reaches its maximum height. That happens around June 21st, defining the start of summer. Conversely, the sun's lowest point defines the winter solstice around December 21st.

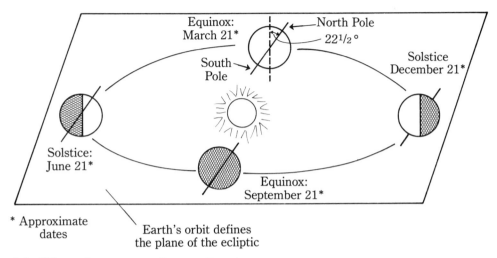

3-8 Why we have seasons. Because Earth's axis is not exactly perpendicular to the ecliptic (defined by the plane of Earth's orbit), our northern and southern hemispheres are alternately "favored" by the sun.

Just the opposite is true in the southern hemisphere, where our summer solstice becomes their winter solstice. For half the year, the northern hemisphere is favored by the sun because we're tilted towards it, while for the rest of the year the sun favors the southern hemisphere. So twice a year there must be moments of change-over when the sun, being directly over the equator, favors both hemispheres equally. We call those moments the *spring* and *fall equinoxes*, literally "equal nights," when the lengths of night and day are the same. The spring equinox (for the northern hemisphere) marks the change from southern to northern favoritism, and vice versa.

Harvest moon

This brings us to the harvest moon, the full moon closest to our fall equinox, about September 21st. That bright moon, rising in the east as the sun sets in the west, has been an aid to farmers harvesting grain for as long as it has been cultivated, going back perhaps 18,000 years in Egypt and the Middle East.

As we've seen, that's fine for farmers in the northern hemisphere, but what about those south of the equator? Do they call the moon closest to their autumnal equinox (which occurs around March 21st) the harvest moon? Or do they see this as just another of their world's northern biases, like the global convention that puts north at the top of maps?

I don't know. I lived in New Zealand for four years, but somehow I must have been occupied with lesser questions. Do Kiwis and Aussies and the rest of those below-the-equator dwellers celebrate their harvest moon in March or in September? (Don't tell me they don't celebrate it. They'll celebrate anything down under.)

Full moon

People frequently accuse the full moon of causing strangeness in the minds of human beings. After all (I've heard it said), it can't be coincidence that the words *lunar* and *lunacy* come from the same root. The idea that people are weirder than usual when the moon is full even gets the nod from arch-sage Ann Landers. In her syndicated column for August 27, 1984, she wrote, "It's true . . . some people get loonier when the moon is full."

Some do and some don't. Overall, there doesn't appear to be anything to this pervasive myth. Every so often, someone comes up with a new study to show evidence of increased lunacy as measured by such disparate statistics as: homicides in Dade County, Florida and in Cleveland, Ohio; fights during professional hockey games; and suicides and traffic accidents nationwide. Then someone else does the analysis rather more scrupulously, and the effect vanishes. This has happened so frequently that the question, "Why do some people act strangely?" should perhaps be changed to, "Why do so many people (about fifty percent) believe that some people act strangely when the moon is full?"

The answer is probably our tendency to selectively notice and recall unusual incidents. I don't tell my friends about not meeting anyone I knew when I went to New York, but I must have told a hundred people about the time my wife recognized her old school friend as we walked off a ferry in Belize, Central America. "Nothing odd occurred during full moon" just doesn't make it as a headline.

"But what about tides?" I'm asked in my classes. If the moon causes ocean tides, and we're seventy percent water, wouldn't it affect us, physically and perhaps mentally? Just barely it would, but you'd be stretching a point. Compare, for instance, the tidal effect of this book with that of the moon when it's overhead. Tidal effects are proportional to the mass of the body causing them divided by the cube root of the distance. So if we assume my book weighs one pound and it's one foot away from you, its tidal effect will be about 12 thousand times that of the moon. (This works with any book, by the way, not just one on astronomy.)

The moon looks full tonight . . . are those werewolves I hear baying in the hills?

Blue moon

Blue moon is the name usually given the second full moon of the month. The interval between successive full moons is a little more than $29\frac{1}{2}$ days, so any month other than February can accommodate two full moons.

What are the odds of a Blue Moon occurring? On average, there are 365.2425 days in a year. Dividing the length of the year by the full moon interval gives us 12.4.

Having 12.4 full moons in 12 months is equivalent to saying that, in an average 19 year period, seven of those years will get 13 full moons a year; so about once every three years we'll get two full moons in one month, and the second one is called "blue" (but really, it isn't).

A lunar miscellany

That orbèd maiden, with white fire laden
Whom mortals call the moon . . .

Percy Bysshe Shelley, *The Cloud*

- The word *moon* shares its roots with month, menopause, menstruation, and measure; all from the Greek meno-, a prefix for month.

- The craters of the moon are generally named after famous people, even the one called Hell. That's Father Maximilian Hell, Hungarian astronomer (1720-1792).

- Galileo likened a meteor crater on the moon to Bohemia, which roughly corresponds to the present-day Praha basin in Czechoslovakia. Geologists now believe that the Praha basin is an ancient meteor crater. Curious that Galileo saw a resemblance 370 years earlier!

- Earlier yet, Leonardo da Vinci correctly surmised why, during any crescent phase of the moon, we can see the *unlit* part of the disc. It's because sunlight is reflected from Earth: Earthshine.

- Although the moon appears to be larger when it's near the horizon than when it's high in the sky, photographs show this to be an optical illusion (almost entirely: the moon is fractionally larger on the horizon due to refraction). However, the moon's apparent size really does change every couple of weeks, by about 10%, as it moves on its elliptical path from the point closest to Earth (perigee) to the point farthest away (apogee).

- The moon is the most important component in creating tides in Earthly oceans. Its influence is half again as much as the sun's.

- With a surface area of 16 million miles, the moon could be wrapped in a cloth cut to the size of North and South America.

- Earth has fifty times the volume and eighty times the mass of the moon.

- The sun and the moon appear to be about the same size to us. During a total eclipse of the sun, when the moon appears to cover the sun, it's a near-perfect fit. That's because, although the diameter of the sun is some 400 times greater than that of the moon, the sun is about 400 times farther away.

- One way to test Albert Einstein's 1905 Special Theory of Relativity is to analyze minuscule changes in the distance between Earth and the moon. The distance is measured by firing a laser beam from an observatory in Texas to reflectors on the moon (left there by Apollo astronauts) and timing exactly how long the echo takes to return. It's a tricky aim, so when an echo is received, a bell rings for positive reinforcement.

- One of the earliest science-fiction tales was "Man in the Moon," written in 1638 by Francis Godwin. In it, the protagonist was towed to the moon by 25 swans, where he had some curious adventures with moon-folks 28 feet tall.

- The same hemisphere of the moon always faces us. Tidal friction over the last 4¹/₂ billion years is responsible for the natural synchronization.

- Earth's rotation is slowing. Tides cause a gradual braking effect on its rotation, causing the length of the day to increase by a couple of milliseconds per century. To conserve angular momentum, the moon recedes from us at about two inches a year.

- The Earth day and lunar month will eventually synchronize—at about 47 days. When this happens, the moon will always be over the same point on the surface of Earth. After that, the distance between Earth and the moon will decrease, until tidal forces cause our satellite to break apart and Earth acquires an orbiting ring of a zillion rocky fragments.

- Not just yet, though.

Flat earth revisited

There would be dangers, of course . . . Not the risk of falling off the edge of the earth or going so far over the rim you couldn't get back: no serious sailor, no one who had seen ships disappear over the horizon and return without incident, could believe that sort of landlubberly twaddle.

Kirkpatrick Sale, *The Conquest of Paradise*, (the story of Christopher Columbus and his legacy)

In a conversation with some young children a few months ago, I discovered that one hoary old myth is still alive and well—the one that says: Everyone thought Columbus would fall off the edge of the world if he sailed westward from Spain. The kids thought most people in 1492 really believed the world was flat, and that Christopher Columbus was doomed from the start.

In reality, it's been common knowledge for at least two thousand years that our home planet is roughly spherical. For instance, around 500 B.C., followers of Pythagoras deduced that Earth was round from its shadow on the moon during a lunar eclipse. In contrast to most later writers (up to the time of Nicholas Copernicus), they didn't believe Earth was the center of the solar system. To be fair, they didn't believe the sun was either, saying that the cosmic center was an unseen fire whose light was reflected by the sun.

Here's how Aristotle explained the Pythagoreans' reasoning for a round Earth: "How else would eclipses of the moon show segments shaped as we see them? As it is, the shapes which the moon itself each month shows are of every kind—straight, gibbous, and concave—but in eclipses the outline is always curved; and, since it is the interposition of the earth that makes the eclipse, the form of this line will be caused by the form of the earth's surface, which is therefore spherical'' (Revised Oxford Translation).

Not only spherical, but we have evidence that those sharp-witted ancients even calculated our planet's size. Their technique was based on the simple fact that at noon on any particular day of the year, the sun's elevation (i.e., how high it appears to be above the horizon) depends solely on how far you are from the equator. That's how a navigational sextant works. We believe this was the method used by a brilliant Greek-educated librarian at Alexandria, Eratosthenes (c.275 – c.175 B.C.).

Eratosthenes knew that at noon on the longest day of the year, the sun was due overhead at present-day Aswan, up-river and about 500 miles south of Alexandria. He observed that at that time, the sun in Alexandria appeared to be about 7¹/₂ degrees from overhead (by measuring the angle an upright stick cast on the ground). Realizing that the distance between Aswan and Alexandria was responsible for the 7¹/₂ degree difference in the sun's elevation and knowing that 7¹/₂ degrees was ¹/₄₈ of a full (360 degree) circle, Eratosthenes simply multiplied the distance between Alexandria and Aswan by 48 to arrive at Earth's circumference.

What's a stade?

How close did he get to the right answer? We're not sure! His answer was 250,000 stades, but what's a stade? Anything from 517 feet (according to the Roman naturalist Pliny) to 689 feet (from measurements in Egypt), which is a rather wide range. If you use the shortest value, his value for Earth's circumference translates to 24,480 miles, less than 2% short of the actual value. If you take the higher value for the stade, he was about 30% on the high side, which still isn't too bad. The point is that Eratosthenes took our planet's spherical shape for granted, and any believers of a flat Earth of his time were probably scoffed at.

Old records imply that models of Earth were in existence in Eratosthenes' time, although they must have shown great empty spaces: terra incognito, unknown land. Nearly 2,000 years were to elapse before navigators like Columbus, Magellan, and Cook set off to fill in those blanks. Today we're accustomed to looking at a map of the world in a (flat) atlas, knowing it's just a representation of the real thing—a two-dimensional surface imperfectly translated from a three-dimensional sphere, which is imperfectly modeled from the real thing, Earth itself. It's like comparing a minuscule black and white photograph of a cat with a small furry animal that purrs when you stroke its ears.

The complete connection was made only a little over 20 years ago, when we saw the first photograph of Earth in its entirety (see the next section, New views of Earth). Until then, we were a little like Columbus and his crew: we knew in our hearts that the world was round, but it was sure nice to have it confirmed.

New views of Earth

To see the earth as we now see it, small and blue and beautiful in that eternal silence where it floats, is to see ourselves as riders on the earth together, brothers on that bright loveliness in the unending night—brothers who see now they are truly brothers.

Archibald MacLeish, *Riders on the Earth* (from *Bubble of Blue Air*)

Two hundred years ago, a craftsman in England created the pocket globe, shown in Fig. 3-9. It is two globes in one: terrestrial and celestial—a view *in* to the surface of Earth, and a view *out* to the stars.

3-9 English "pocket globe" from about 1765, with the routes of several voyages of exploration. The case is lined with a celestial map, showing constellations.

If we want to visualize the whole of the three-dimensional sphere we call Earth, a flat two-dimensional map doesn't cut it. A regular map is fine for small areas and even whole continents, but after a while the distortion becomes so great, you really need to move up a dimension. This fact has been appreciated for centuries. The ancient Mesopotamians and Egyptians probably made celestial globes of stone and copper, and there's good evidence that Crates of Mallus, a Greek astronomer, made a terrestrial globe in the second century B.C.

The oldest existing globe is believed to be that made by Martin Behaim in Nuremberg, Germany, in 1492. It's 20 inches in diameter, has 1,100 place names on it, and can be seen in the Germanic Museum in Nuremberg. Despite Eratosthenes' respectable estimate of the circumference of Earth 18 centuries earlier (see *Flat Earth revisited*), the Behaim Globe shows the distance from the Canaries to Cipango (Japan) to be less than 3,000 miles, or about 7,000 miles shy of the actual distance! No wonder Columbus named the islands on which he made landfall in the same year the "West Indies."

The beauty of the pocket globe (made nearly three centuries later) is the implied continuity of space from Earth to the stars by combining the two models into one handy, portable object: a marvel of complexity and compactness.

The first color view of Earth

On November 10, 1967, a satellite in orbit above Brazil sent us our first color picture of the whole Earth (see C-5). The satellite, named ATS-3, is in geosynchronous orbit—that is, it orbits Earth in exactly 24 hours, constantly remaining over the same location on Earth's surface. Any object in a circular orbit 22,000 miles above the equator can't do anything else, as Newton could have told us.

Could have, but didn't—that was left to the prescience of science fiction writer Arthur C. Clarke. When you point your TV dish towards some spot in the southern sky (assuming you have a dish and that you live north of the equator), you're taking advantage of that fact. Your dish is locked on to a relay satellite that appears to hang motionless at a distance nearly one tenth that of the moon, apparently—but not really—defying gravity.

So here's the picture, a feast for the heart, showing a fragile disc of blue and white and brown against the black void of space. It's the only planet we've got, and this picture was the first of many graphic reminders. Photographs of the whole Earth are now common. It's a far cry from 1948, when astronomer Fred Hoyle anticipated the reaction such views would evoke when they were first published. He then wrote, "Once a photograph of the earth, taken from outside, is available, once the sheer isolation of the earth becomes plain, a new idea as powerful as any in history will be let loose."

Winning our minds

If that image from 1967 won our hearts, I believe GeoSphere will win our minds. The GeoSphere is a globe seven feet in diameter residing in Santa Monica, California. A 2-dimensional reproduction of it appears as Fig. C-6, although by the time you read this, actual three-dimensional globes might be on the market. Look at the reproduction carefully. It is, and it isn't, the real live Earth.

The most obvious feature is that it is cloud-free, as opposed to the ATS-3 picture, or any picture, of Earth from space. With a total of about 3,000 cubic miles of water vapor constantly present in the atmosphere, it's not surprising that a major portion of our planet is always covered by clouds. Not only are there no clouds in the GeoSphere image, there's no night and no winter either. It's as if the sun is simultaneously over both the northern and southern hemispheres. (One exception: land over 10,000 feet is shown as snow covered.) Another feature setting Geosphere apart is the degree of detail: it contains 36.3 million color pixels (picture elements), compared to a standard TV's 128,000. In the size we've been able to reproduce here, such detail hardly shows; but in the large globe, the resolution is a fine 4 kilometers (soon to be 1 km., with 16 times more detail).

GeoSphere is the result of 2,400 hours of work by a team of computer experts working under artist Tom Van Sant (Fig. 3-10) and computer-graphics specialist Lloyd Van Warren. To create the necessary database, they used over 2,000 photo-

Tom Van Sant /The GeoSphere Project, Santa Monica, CA

3-10   The seven-foot GeoSphere and its creator, Tom Van Sant.

graphs from weather satellites. Where they couldn't find a complete cloud-free photo, they "borrowed" parts of other photos to fill in the obscured areas.

The new global map is exciting enough as it is, but there's more to come. With all the information computerized and tied into global data bases, the plan is to extend its use so that complex global issues can be visualized and understood. Future uses will include investigation of global weather and climatic changes, large-scale forest and crop inventories, population distribution and migration, biological diversity and species depletion, and vegetation band migration.

According to Van Sant, GeoSphere technology will eventually be able to show, "what the Amazon region looked like in 1972, 1982 and show what it looks like [today]. With risk projection, we can show what the rain forests will look like in 2010 given the same rate of deforestation."

A new way of seeing Earth isn't unprecedented. It happened suddenly with the ATS-3 picture in 1967, and it happened slowly (over 300 years) from Columbus' voyage to the New World, to navigators like Magellan, da Gama, and later, Cook. Between them, they created the databases that allowed cartographers to map the planet accurately for the first time. New ways of looking at our home in space do not happen often, and this one is cause enough for global celebration.

What goes round what?

As you know, the name "cosmos" is given by most astronomers to the sphere whose center is the Earth, and whose radius is equal to the distance between the centers of the Earth and the Sun; this you have seen in the treatises written by astronomers.

But Aristarchus of Samos published a book of speculations, in which the initial assumptions led to the conclusion that the whole universe is very much larger than what is now called the cosmos. He supposes that the fixed stars and the sun are stationary, that the Earth travels round the sun along the circumference of a circle . . . and that the sphere of the fixed stars is so vast in extent that—by comparison—the supposed circular orbit of the Earth is, in effect, no larger than the central point of a sphere compared with its surface.

Archimedes, *The Sand Reckoner,* **c. 230** B.C.

The front page headline of my morning paper read "Many Think Sun Circles the Earth." Over 2,000 people were asked, among other questions, "Does the Earth go around the sun or the sun around the Earth?" Twenty-one percent of those gave the wrong answer, and seven percent didn't know. It only took a couple of days for the letters to appear stating along the lines of, "It depends on your point of view," defending the seven percent "don't knowers."

From the sun's point of view, Earth does indeed appear to orbit it. However, as one wag pointed out, most of us don't make our observations from the sun, we make them from Earth. From *our* perspective, it does look as if the sun orbits us. Convincing people that it was the other way around was the problem Copernicus was faced with. His cop-out solution was to allow his book promoting a sun-centered system, *Concerning the Revolutions of the Celestial Spheres,* to be published only when he was on his deathbed in 1543.

Consider what the situation would be if the sun and Earth were the only bodies in the universe. Without any preferred frame of reference, neither one would be an obvious candidate for the "center." Only when you put in the other planets and the background stars does it become apparent that Earth "really" orbits the sun, rather than the other way abound. (Purists would say that they both orbit the center of mass of the two-body system, but that's so close to the sun's center that we can ignore them for this discussion.)

However, the sun and Earth aren't the only bodies in the universe, and any reasonable, non-nitpicking observer of the solar system would have no doubt: the sun is at the center. We go around it, along with the other planets. Period.

But who proved it?

Back to the newspaper story. It begins, "More than 450 years after Copernicus proved that Earth revolves around the sun . . ." Now here is an issue worthy of debate. First, he was by no means the first to have advanced the concept of a sun-centered, or heliocentric, system. Around 270 B.C., Aristarchus of Samos put the sun at the center of things, as we see from the quotation that begins this essay, with which Copernicus was probably familiar. Nicholas of Oresme in the four-teenth century and Nicholas of Cusa in the fifteenth also promoted heliocentrism, although these were exceptions to the rule.

Second, if anyone could be said to have *proved* that planets revolve around the sun, the credit should go to Galileo who built his first telescope nearly 70 years after Copernicus' death. He noticed that Venus wasn't a uniformly round disc, but rather went through phases just like the moon did. He also noted that the thinner the crescent, the greater its diameter, while the fullest disc was smallest (See *Morning and evening stars: Mercury and Venus* and Fig. 4-4). His genius was to realize that this is exactly what you'd expect if both Venus and Earth orbited the sun, and it explained the changes in brightness of Venus that had puzzled pretele-scopic observers.

News of this observation, more than anything else, convinced doubters that the Aristachus-Copernicus theory was correct. The details were still being worked out (Copernicus assumed planets revolved in circular orbits, and it was Kepler who realized they were actually elliptical), but Galileo offered the proof for what had been only speculation until then.

All this was long ago and far away, yet here—in the largest industrialized coun-try in the world—we can still wake up to headlines like the one quoted above. It's scary. Democracies depend on an informed public to operate, and if we as a nation are not sure of basic facts of life, such as our place in space, we're in for a rocky future.

More and more, scientific and technological issues dominate national debate, from the greenhouse effect to the economic threat from foreign technology. Being able to understand these debates is becoming as important to you as being able to read.

Robert Hazen and James Trefil, *Science Matters*

Blue skies and red sunrises

. . . the night's grand finale: the shifting colors that played on the sky from behind the earth before the rising of the sun.

Paul Bowles, *The Sheltering Sky*

Why is the sky blue? It's one of the most persistent questions I'm asked in my introductory astronomy classes, and it's one that lends itself to a wealth of misun-derstanding. The answer relates to how easily different colors of light negotiate their way through Earth's atmosphere.

Light from the sun comes in a wide spectrum of colors: red, orange, yellow, green, blue, indigo, violet, or ROYGBIV, if you remember your high-school mne-monic. Put together, it all looks white.

One way of thinking about light is as waves, like waves on the ocean. When the crests are far apart, they have a long *wavelength*, and vice versa. The more energetic of the colors—the ones towards the blue end of the spectrum—have shorter wavelengths, which makes them more susceptible to being scattered in the atmosphere. (It's called *Rayleigh Scattering*, after English physicist, John Rayleigh.)

Why are short wavelengths of light more likely to be scattered than longer wavelengths? Consider this analogy: You're bouncing a ball as you walk down a concrete sidewalk. The sidewalk is full of cracks. The more often you bounce the ball, the more likely you are to hit a crack, causing the ball to go off course. The more frequently it is bounced, the shorter the distance between "crests." That's the rule: the more frequent the bounce, the shorter the wavelength, and the greater the chance of hitting a crack. Like your ball, the short, high-energy, blue wavelengths are more likely to encounter, not cracks, but water molecules or dust particles in the upper atmosphere.

Warning: This is an imprecise analogy. Air molecules are actually thousands of times smaller than the wavelength of visible light. However, it should suffice until you're ready to check out electron resonances.

So sunlight, which starts out as white (ask any astronaut who has been above Earth's atmosphere), loses some of its blue light as it comes down through the atmosphere; thus, we see the sun as slightly yellow. (We do, but we shouldn't. Remember, it's what we don't see that hurts us. The sun's ultraviolet rays are invisible, but deadly to the sensitive cells in the retinas of our eyes. *Never look directly at the sun.*)

What happens to the scattered blue light? It ends up all over the place. We're usually only aware of it after it's bounced all over the atmosphere, eventually rebounding down to Earth's surface. That's why the sky appears blue.

Red sky at night . . .

Follow-up question: why are sunrises and sunsets red? No doubt about it, the sun appears to be a different color when it's rising and setting than when it's high in the sky. Figure 3-11 should explain it, now that you've got the hang of how the atmosphere scatters out the sun's blue wavelengths. The farther sunlight has to travel through the atmosphere, the more blue is removed, and the redder the sun appears.

In the moon's shadow

Between the idea
And the reality
Between the motion
And the act
Falls the Shadow.

T.S. Eliot, *The Hollow Men*.

I thought I knew about total eclipses of the sun. After all, I'd been reading about them for decades, I'd looked at hundreds of photographs of eclipses, and discussed them at length in my astronomy classes. I had once written: "We watched a series of slides as the moon moved across the face of the sun, until only the so-called 'dia-

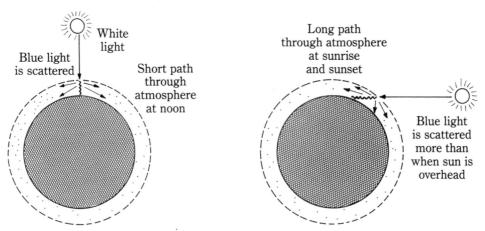

3-11   Why the sky is red at sunrise and sunset.

mond rings' were left. These are the final glimpses of the sun's disk seen through valleys on the moonlimb, before the sun disappears completely. At the moment of disappearance, the sun's corona, or outer atmosphere, becomes visible in its glory, a soft aura of light around the moon. Then too, for those few seconds of totality, prominences of hydrogen gas can be seen if they present. And for the eclipse of last March, they were indeed present, arching above the sun's surface to a height corresponding to ten Earth diameters! The photographers captured these unusually fine displays." I wrote this after attending a slide show by veteran eclipse-chaser Jacques Guertin, who'd witnessed the March 1988 total solar eclipse from Borneo.

Doesn't that sound as if I'd know what to expect when viewing my first total eclipse, from Baja, California, on July 11, 1991? The fact is, I didn't have a clue. Those six minutes and fifty two seconds of totality caught me utterly unprepared. My life is now divided into BE and AE (Before Eclipse and After Eclipse). It was all shockingly beautiful, in particular the ruby-red prominences and the vast size of the corona.

Getting there, they say, is half the fun. It certainly was an experience. My wife Louisa and I, along with our pilot (who had answered my ad posted at the local flying club) and his friend, newly-arrived from Germany, all squeezed into a Cessna 172 in Palo Alto, California five days before the eclipse. Three days and many adventures later, we landed at Los Friales, Baja. Why Los Friales (not generally known as a center of world culture)? Because it had the closest airstrip to the eclipse centerline on Baja's eastern coast.

By the morning of July 11, we were well organized. My four-inch refractor telescope was ready in the "observatory" (a patch of sand protected from the wind by a tarpaulin), and I saw first contact, the moment when the moon's disk began its traverse across the face of the sun, right on time. An hour later, with two-thirds of the sun's disk covered, the temperature had dropped noticeably and the light was slightly dimmer. The cacti took on a pastel color.

Minutes later, other subtle changes occurred. We saw and heard birds, usually quiet at noon in that arid climate, as they began to wake up in this pseudosunset. Shadows became sharp, so that I saw individual hairs on my head silhouetted on the sand at my feet. Hundreds of little crescents could be seen beneath a straw hat, whose holes focused the sun, reminiscent of the way a pin-hole camera works (Figs. 3-12 and 3-13). Then, right on time, the mountains to the west suddenly darkened as the moon's shadow, racing at 1,300 mph across our planet, cut sunlight off from the peaks. Seconds later, as if someone had turned a switch, it happened: we were in totality.

It was far from pitch-darkness (admonitions to have flashlights handy proved unnecessary), but the abruptness of the transition from the sun being just visible to totality was a shock to us all, no matter how well prepared we were. Overhead, the white wreath of the corona, much larger than we'd expected, extended two or three sun diameters from what appeared to be a round black hole in the sky. With the naked eye, we could just make out prominences of hot gas. Through the telescope, they were awesome: two bright ruby-red arches opposite each other, one reaching up to a height of at least ten Earth-diameters from the solar "surface" (Figs. C-2 and C-3).

The minutes whizzed by and then, far too soon, came the moment of the sun's return. I was looking through my telescope when first a single bead of sunlight, then an avalanche of photons, an incandescent blast, hit my retina: it was overtime

Photo by author

3-12 Baja, California, July 11, 1991. Whiling away the minutes as eclipse totality approached. Pinholes in the straw hat focus the sun's image on a piece of card.

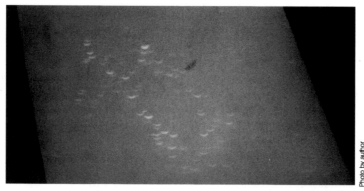

Photo by author

3-13 Dozens of images of the three-quarters eclipsed sun.

to replace the mylar solar screen. We'd read previously that people generally cheered when the sun returned. Not our little party. We looked at each other with the expressions of those who had seen a miracle, and weren't ready for it to be over. Inevitably the first words following totality were spoken: "When's the next one?"

Total solar eclipses, 1990 – 1999

Date	Maximum duration	Location
7/22/90	2m 36s	Northern Europe
7/11/91	6m 58s	Hawaii, Mexico, Central & South America
6/30/92	5m 26s	South Atlantic
11/3/94	4m 28s	South America, South Atlantic
10/24/95	2m 15s	Southern Asia, Western Pacific
3/9/97	2m 54s	Siberia
2/26/98	4m 13s	Central & South America, Caribbean
8/11/99	2m 27s	Central Europe, Asia

The next total solar eclipse over the continental United States will occur on August 21, 2017. See you there.

Eclipse miscellany

24 us [96 minutes] after sunrise, a solar eclipse [obscured the sun] on the southwest side when it began. Venus and Mercury . . . were visible; Jupiter and Mars, which were in their period of disappearance [i.e., not visible at night] were visible in that eclipse . . . [The shadow] moved from southwest to northeast.

Babylonian record (now in the British Museum) for eclipse of April 15, 136 B.C., adapted from translation by A.J. Sachs

- The word *eclipse* comes from the Greek ekleipsis, meaning omission or failure, that is, something gone wrong. It's cognate with *ellipse* and with *ellipsis*, those quaint periods . . . found in novels where something (usually racy) is omitted.

- The moon's orbit is tilted with respect to the ecliptic, the plane of Earth's orbit around the sun, by about five degrees. If it weren't tilted, but was in the same plane, we'd experience many more eclipses: a solar eclipse every new moon and a lunar eclipse every full moon.

- In a lifetime of "three score years and ten" and with clear skies, a person can expect to see (from the same location) about 50 lunar eclipses (half being total) and 30 partial solar eclipses. However, he or she would only have a one in five chance of seeing a total solar eclipse.

- Even when the sun, moon, and Earth are exactly in line, we're still not guaranteed a *total* solar eclipse. The moon is in an elliptical orbit, its distance varying from about 220 to 250 thousand miles. When the moon is farthest from us (at its apogee), Earth is beyond its conical shadow (the umbra). In this case, from our point of view, the moon is too small to completely cover the sun's disk and instead of totality, we see a ring of sunlight: an annular eclipse. Pretty, but not the real thing.

- The longest possible duration of a total solar eclipse is 7 minutes 40 seconds; and of a total lunar eclipse, 1 hour 44 minutes.

- People have been noting eclipses for a long time. The Greek astronomer, Ptolemy, writing in the second century A.D., discusses Babylonian eclipse records going back to 747 B.C.

- Thales of Miletus predicted the year for the eclipse of May 28, 585 B.C., according to Herodotus. He probably did so using the Saros cycle discovered by the Babylonians. A mathematical coincidence results in approximately the same configuration of the sun, moon, and Earth every 18 years $11\frac{1}{3}$ days (ignoring Leap Years).

- That 585 B.C. eclipse probably gives us the first definitive date for a historical event, the end of a war. The Lydians and Medes were in the middle of a battle when, says Herodotus, "the day was suddenly turned to night . . . so they ceased from fighting, and both were the more zealous to make peace."

- The old Chinese pictogram for a total eclipse, *chi*, showed a man turning his head away from a plate of food, indicating he was full.

- The ancient Chinese related the fortunes of the emperor and his family to eclipses. The record for the total solar eclipse of January 18, A.D. 120 includes the commentary, "The woman showed aversion to it. Two years and three months later, Teng, the Empress Dowager, died."

- The length of the day is increasing by nearly two milliseconds per century, mainly due to the braking effect of tides. Those ancient eclipse records help astronomers calculate exactly how fast Earth is slowing. If the length of the day were constant, present-day calculations show that you would have had to be at least 2,500 miles from Babylon to see the total solar eclipse of April 15, 136 B.C., but it *was* seen in Babylon, according to two tablets now the British Museum (see quote at the start of this essay). The rate of slowing is thus given by those 2,500 miles "lost" over 21 centuries.

4
The inner planets

It is the opinion of all the modern philosophers and mathematicians that the planets are habitable worlds.

Benjamin Franklin, *Poor Richard's Almanac*, 1749

Introduction to the inner planets

The solar system is conveniently divided into inner and outer regions with a belt of rocks, the asteroids, between Mars and Jupiter forming the boundary. The inner solar system consists of four comparatively small, solid, planets: Mercury, Venus, Earth and Mars, with three moons between them. The outer solar system consists of four large "gas balls" (probably with small rocky cores): Jupiter, Saturn, Uranus and Neptune, with a total of about sixty moons. (Tiny, icy Pluto is the exception to all this, as usual.)

Because the sun and planets all formed from the same cloud of interstellar gas and dust, it's reasonable to assume they had the same constituents available at their birth. Also, because the sun consists of about 75% hydrogen and 25% helium, with just a trace of heavier elements thrown in, you might ask why we—not to mention Mercury, Venus and Mars—don't consist of the same ingredients.

The reason is that planets with such a composition aren't stable close to the sun. Gaseous hydrogen and helium would have been both evaporated by the sun's heat and driven off by the solar wind (a million mile an hour gale of charged particles) early in the history of the solar system. Farther from the sun, the gas giants Jupiter, Saturn, Uranus, and Neptune *are* stable. They might resemble our Earth overlain with immensely thick coverings of ice and gas. Such coverings would have been swept away had the planets evolved closer to the sun.

Vulnerable Mercury

If the sun evaporated and swept hydrogen and helium from proto-Venus, Earth, and Mars, imagine what it must have done to Mercury, the closest (and therefore the most vulnerable) planet to the sun. Whereas Venus, Earth, and Mars are composed essentially of small iron cores with thick silicate (rocky) mantles above, Mercury is just the opposite: a comparatively large iron core with a thin silicate mantle.

If Mercury's core *had* once been covered with a thick rocky mantle, that too would have been evaporated by the sun billions of years ago.

Mercury is small, about half as large as our moon. Its surface also looks very much like the moon's highland terrain with pristine craters (Fig. 4-1). Mercury's long days and proximity to the sun give it the largest temperature difference of any object in the solar system (from minus 400 to plus 600 °F). Like our moon, it has no atmosphere and no erosion. Internally, its massive iron core is probably still cooling and shrinking. This could explain the long, wrinkled ridges on the surface of the planet seen by the Mariner 10 spacecraft, which flew by in March 1974.

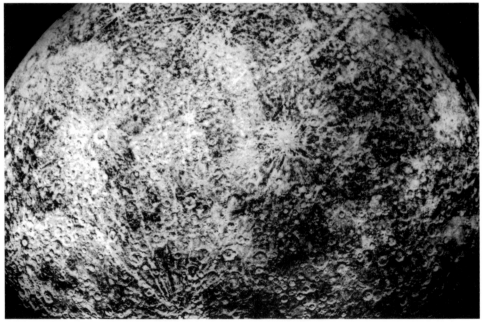

4-1 Mercury. Looking much like the highlands of our moon, fresh-looking craters from impacts which occurred billions of years ago testify to the stability of Mercury: no volcanoes and very little crustal movement.

One boiled while the other froze

Although there's little resemblance today, many scientists believe Venus, Earth, and Mars had similar surface conditions when the solar system was young and when the sun was putting out 30% less energy than it does today. The three planets had similar minerals on their surfaces, similar gases in their atmospheres (mainly carbon dioxide), and all were sufficiently temperate to support oceans of liquid water. In other words, all three possessed conditions ripe for the start of life. Later, however, Venus boiled and Mars froze, while conditions on Earth stayed much the same. Why? The answer to this, the so-called Goldilocks problem of climatology, occupies much of this section. ("Goldilocks," you might remember, preferred things in the middle, neither too hot nor too large, too cold nor too small.)

Much appears to hinge on the presence of carbon dioxide. This gas is largely responsible for the warming "greenhouse effect," discussed in the next few pages. Earth seems to have always enjoyed a moderate climate due to a wondrous automatic feedback mechanism: more carbon dioxide is cycled into the atmosphere when the surface is cool (so the surface warms up), and less when the surface is hot (so it cools down).

Because of its comparatively small size, Mars virtually stopped cycling the gas billions of years ago. Most of its carbon dioxide is trapped in the rocks and soil, resulting in freezing conditions at the surface. Venus' carbon dioxide is also trapped, but it's stuck in the atmosphere. This caused the planet to heat up in a runaway greenhouse effect. On Mars, you could at least walk around in a spacesuit, but on Venus you'd be fried, crushed, and eaten to death by the acidic atmosphere. That's why Mars is a prime candidate for the next manned expedition into space, and why Venus just doesn't rate. Given time and the will to do so, we might even be able to turn Mars into another Earth-like planet, in a process called *terraforming*.

Earth, Venus, and Mars are generally believed to have accreted from dry, rocky planetisimals orbiting the newly switched-on sun 4.6 billion years ago. Later, the three planets received a literal flood of a very different class of planetisimals, which originated in the outer solar system in the region of Uranus and Neptune. These secondary arrivals hadn't been "cooked" by the sun, and so were your basic volatile-rich comets (or "tar-balls," according to one planetary scientist).

Were organic (carbon-based) materials brought to Earth by countless cometary impacts? Is this how life got started? If so, what happened on Venus and Mars, where presumably the same thing was happening?

These issues are hot scientific debate topics in the 1990s. The answers won't come all at once. More data is coming from Venus, currently being mapped to a high resolution by an orbiting radar-equipped spacecraft (Magellan); plans are underway to further explore Mars, including the retrieval of samples from the surface for analysis on Earth; and, unraveling the biggest puzzle of all, advances in bioengineering are starting to explain how nature created life from its constituents.

It's a great time to watch, and perhaps participate in, the solving of the mysteries of the terrestrial planets, in particular Venus and Mars.

The greenhouse effect

The earth's atmosphere has never been free of change . . . Yet the pace in the past two centuries has been remarkable: the atmosphere's composition in particular has changed significantly faster than it has at any time in human history.

Thomas E. Graedel & Paul J. Crutzen, *Scientific American*,
September 1989

One major effect of the industrial revolution has been a 25% increase in the concentration of carbon dioxide in Earth's atmosphere, through the burning of coal, oil, and other fossil fuels and wholesale destruction of forests. Why does the amount of carbon dioxide affect us at all? Because of the greenhouse effect, a key phenomenon in understanding the climates of three of the "terrestrial" planets, Earth, Venus, and Mars. So before we go on to examine what happened to our sister planets billions of years ago, here's a quick tutorial.

The easiest way to understand the greenhouse effect is, naturally, to look at a greenhouse. Sunlight penetrates the greenhouse glass and heats up the soil and plants inside, which, being warm, radiate invisible infrared light. (Just like an electric stove's heating element that radiates in the infrared when it is first switched on, before it starts radiating in the visible red light spectrum, where you can see the heat. You can feel it but you can't see it.)

You might suppose the infrared energy would simply radiate back through the glass, so any energy entering the greenhouse would also leave it. It doesn't, however. Instead, it stays inside the greenhouse, raising the internal temperature and creating a warm environment for the plants. Why doesn't the infrared radiation from the plants escape? Because glass, which is transparent to sunlight in the visible portion of the spectrum, is opaque to infrared radiation. It's like a one-way mirror: sunlight can get in, but infrared radiation can't get out.

On a global scale, our atmosphere takes the place of greenhouse glass. Sunlight gets in alright, but most of the heat doesn't get out. Carbon dioxide in the atmosphere (with an assist from water vapor) acts as a blanket to prevent infrared energy from escaping, and in the process makes Earth habitable.

The odd thing is how little carbon dioxide our atmosphere contains: only about one part in 3,000! It's a case of quality over quantity. Because so little of the gas has such a major effect, you can see why the comparatively small volume of carbon dioxide added each year to the atmosphere might produce such a large warming effect on our climate. On the other hand, without greenhouse gases, Earth would be about 70 degrees Fahrenheit colder than it actually is. Figure 4-2 summarizes the mechanism.

Morning and evening stars: Mercury and Venus

The Mother of the Loves imitates the phases of Cynthia.

Galileo, letter to Kepler, 1610. (Originally sent as an anagram, a device frequently used to protect the information while establishing primacy of discovery): Venus is the Mother of the Loves, the moon is Cynthia. He's saying that Venus has phases similar to the moon's.

Mercury and Venus are not stars at all, they're planets—two of the four that make up the "inner solar system" (Earth and Mars are the other two). Tiny, rocky Mercury is the closest planet to the sun, with Venus next. Because they're both inside Earth's orbit, they never appear to be very high in the sky, unlike the other planets that can appear overhead.

Take a look at Fig. 4-3 to see how it works. Venus is shown at the position in its orbit when it appears furthest from the sun as seen from Earth. The angle E_v is

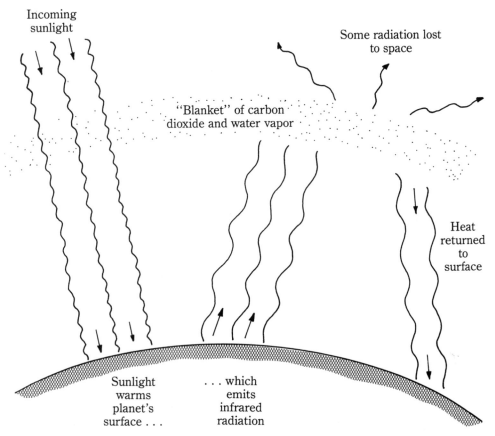

Incoming sunlight

Some radiation lost to space

"Blanket" of carbon dioxide and water vapor

Heat returned to surface

Sunlight warms planet's surface . . .

. . . which emits infrared radiation

4-2 The greenhouse effect. Visible light from the sun heats the surface, which thus radiates in infrared wavelengths. Carbon dioxide and water vapor, which allow visible light to pass through, trap much of this infrared, which is then re-radiated back to the surface.

Venus' maximum elongation, about 46 degrees. Similarly E_M, Mercury's maximum elongation, is about 28 degrees (it's quite variable, because Mercury orbits in a very elliptical path compared to Venus' and Earth's near-circular orbits).

This means that Mercury is very hard to see, because it's never far above the horizon and is always in the same general direction as the sun when the latter is setting or rising. Not only is Mercury usually lost in the sun's glare, but it's very small, just forty percent larger than the moon.

Venus is a lot easier to spot. It's big, about the size of Earth. It's also bright because with an albedo (see Glossary) of 0.65, it reflects about two-thirds of sunlight (Mercury, albedo 0.11, reflects a little more than one tenth, the same as our moon). Also because Venus' elongation can reach 47 degrees, it might set several hours after the sun sets (or rise several hours before the sun rises). For this reason, Venus is known as the evening (or morning) star, and presumably why many sightings of UFOs turn out, on closer inspection, to be sightings of our sister planet.

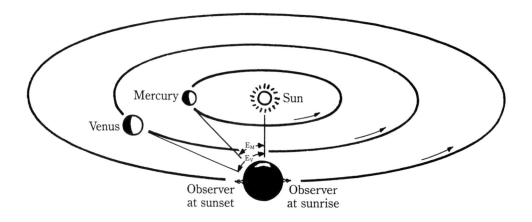

E_M is Mercury's greatest elongation
E_V is Venus' greatest elongation

4-3   Elongation of Mercury & Venus. Both planets orbit inside Earth's orbit, so to us they never appear far from the sun. Their greatest angular distance from the sun (called *elongation*), is: Mercury 28 degrees; Venus, 47 degrees.

Confirming Galileo

It's easy to show, as did Galileo in 1610, that Venus and Earth both orbit the sun. Copernicus *said* they did, but many people were still skeptical.

Seen through a telescope, Venus has an appreciable size. What Galileo noticed—and I hope you will, too, by following the planet with binoculars over a period of time—is that as the size of Venus varies, so does its shape. When it's near maximum elongation, it appears much as the quarter or three-quarter moon does, illuminated on its sunward-facing side, and dark (therefore invisible) on its side away from the sun. When Venus is close to us in its orbit, we see a crescent, and when it's on the far side of the sun, we see it as a nearly full disk (i.e., gibbous). Following in Galileo's footsteps, you'll also notice that its size changes greatly: when closest to us, it appears six times bigger than when it's farthest from us (Fig. 4-4).

The only reasonable way to reconcile these regular changes in size and shape is to adopt Copernicus' sun-centered model of the solar system. Such observations of Venus were just one more nail in the coffin of Ptolemy's Earth-centered cosmos, which ruled supreme for 1,400 years.

Mars: Nearly a living planet

The only reason Mars froze is that it was too small to continue recycling carbon dioxide. An earth-size planet at the orbit of Mars should [have an]

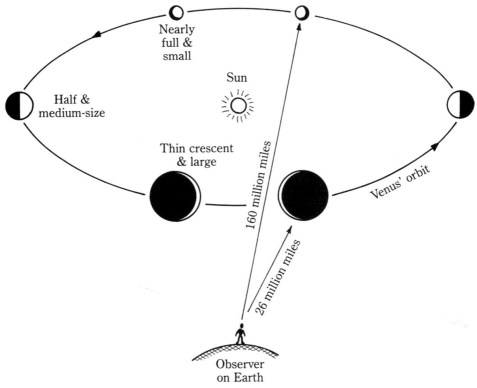

4-4 The phases of Venus, that is, how the sunlit side of the planet appears from Earth. Galileo's observations of the correspondence between Venus' phase and size were convincing evidence that both Venus and the Earth orbited the sun.

> *atmosphere [that] would not be breathable by human beings, but it would be perfectly capable of supporting some sort of life.*
> **James Kasting, Owen Toon & James Pollack, *Scientific American*, February 1988.**

A few billion years ago, Mars might have had oceans and an atmosphere. Compare the mosaic assembled from Viking orbiter photographs (Fig. 4-5, and its key to the main features, Fig. 4-6) with C-7. Covering the same region of Mars as does the mosaic, the color plate is an artist's plausible concept of how Mars might have looked about 3.8 billion years ago. That's when Martian conditions might have been similar to those on Earth.

Most investigators believe that life arose rather quickly once the crust of our planet had cooled down following Earth's formation. If the speed with which life occurred—given sufficiently temperate conditions—is telling us that life can *easily* arise in such conditions, then the chances that life once arose on Mars are quite good. Unfortunately, the chances of it surviving until the present time are virtually negligible.

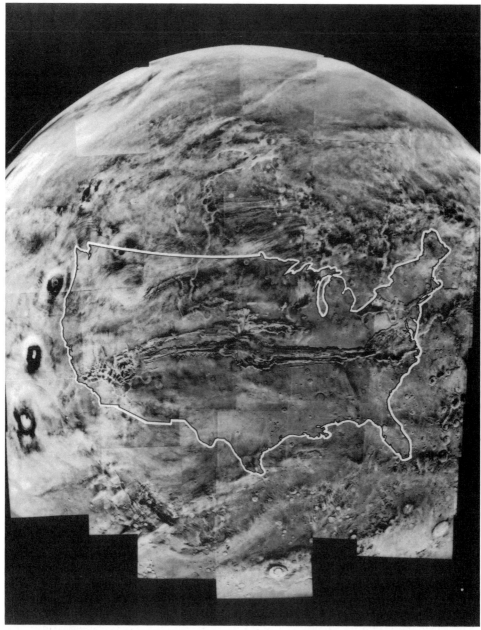

NASA

4-5 Mars' Valles Marineris, with the United States superimposed, to give an idea of the immense size of the valley system. This is one of the "canals" noted by sharp-eyed observers over a hundred years ago. It probably owes its existence to the three volcanoes west of the valley—Arsia Mons, Pavonis Mons and Ascraeus Mons—which might have drawn magma from under the valley floor, leading to its collapse. Similar features are seen in East Africa's rift valley.

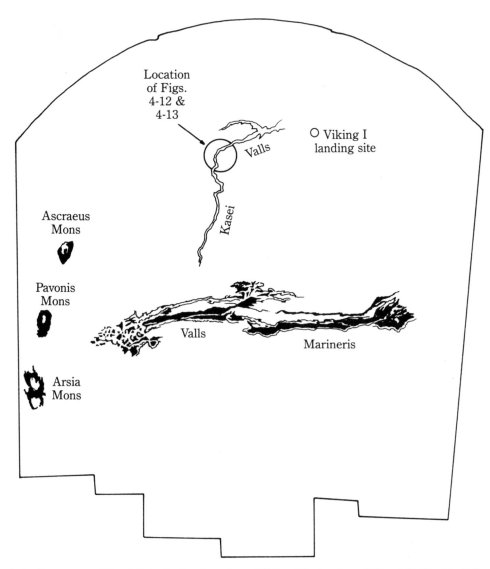

4-6 Key map to Fig. 4-5, including location of Valles Marineris and Kasei Vallis. North is up. Olympus Mons is about 1,000 miles northwest of Pavonis Mons, which is on the Martian equator.

Before we delve into the whys and hows, let's first look at basics. Mars is a rocky planet orbiting the sun every two years at an average distance 1¹/₂ times that of Earth. Its diameter is about half that of Earth's and twice that of the moon, and its surface gravity is 38% of what you're experiencing right now.

A Martian day is about the same length as ours, and the planet's poles are tilted a little more than Earth's, resulting in seasons that vary much as ours do, only over a two-year period. Mars is less dense than Earth, so the subsurface material is probably more permeable, with somewhat greater ability to store water, than here. Altogether, it doesn't sound that bad.

The climate is something else. We received daily weather reports from our Viking surrogates for several years, so we know something about surface conditions. It's usually very cold, as low as −225°F. Sometimes it gets quite warm (above freezing even), but that's right at the surface. The atmosphere is very thin (equivalent to that 20 miles about Earth's surface) and can't conduct much heat, so you're back to below freezing just a foot or so above the surface. What little air there is swirls around at up to 200 mph, periodically raising great dust storms hiding the surface from our view. The air is unbreathable anyway, being ninety percent carbon dioxide.

A kinder, gentler Mars

That ninety percent carbon dioxide content is a clue to what Mars was once like. Most planetary scientists believe Mars once had a thick carbon dioxide atmosphere, sufficiently dense to retain heat (through the greenhouse effect) and allow liquid water to exist. The proof is in the seeing: it's hard to imagine how ancient channels like those in Fig. 4-7 could have been created by anything but water. This

4-7 Evidence for water on Mars' southern highlands. Although a few geologists still caution that networks of channels like these can be explained by faulting and wind erosion, the overwhelming consensus is that water once flowed here. The age of the channels can be estimated by the large impact craters, which virtually ceased being formed about 3.8 billion years ago. The largest crater is about 20 miles in diameter.

mosaic, taken by the Viking orbiters, reminds me of aerial photographs of the deltas of the Nile or Mississippi.

So we're virtually certain water was once abundant on Mars. We also know that those networks of channels were fixed, in the configuration we see now, nearly 4 billion years ago. How do we know? Because huge impact craters overlay the channels (you can see them in the figure), and heavy bombardments of meteorites in the solar system had virtually ended by about 3.8 billion years ago. We also know from studies closer to home that Earth had similar conditions at that time: liquid water under an atmosphere of carbon dioxide.

What happened? Why didn't Mars remain at a temperature at which water could stay liquid? Where did the carbon dioxide and water go? In other words, if Mars was like Earth *then*, why isn't it more like Earth *now*, with carbon dioxide in lieu of our nitrogen/oxygen atmosphere?

It's tempting to think the reason is simply that Mars orbits farther out than we do, but the distance from the sun turns out to be largely a red herring. To illustrate this point, consider two facts: one, Venus receives twice as much solar radiation as Earth, yet it actually retains less solar energy than Earth does (because its sulfuric acid clouds reflect 80% of sunlight before it reaches the surface); two, 4 billion years ago, when the sun's heat was 30% less than it is now, Earth had liquid water in abundance—and so did Mars judging from the Viking photos. It seems that distance from the sun doesn't have much to do with it.

The bigger they are, the hotter they are

The generally-accepted answer is that Mars, with one sixth the volume of Earth, and a "surface area to volume" ratio twice that of Earth, not only started out with less heat than we did, but it lost it faster. It seems that Earth and Mars both began with a carbon dioxide blanket, so the greenhouse effect functioned on both planets. Mars' problem was that carbon dioxide doesn't just sit in the atmosphere, but is weathered out into carbonate rocks, such as limestone.

To maintain a greenhouse effect, you need a mechanism to return the gas from the rocks to the atmosphere, the so-called *carbonate-silicate* geochemical cycle. This works by burying or subducting the carbonate rocks deep below ground, where high temperatures and pressures melt them, resulting in carbon dioxide-rich volcanoes erupting the gas back into the atmosphere. Additionally, in the early days of the solar system when meteorites were very common, carbon dioxide was released each time a rock-shattering and rock-melting impact occurred.

After a billion years or so, these two mechanisms for recycling carbon dioxide virtually ceased: the interior of Mars had lost so much of its heat that it became too cold for volcanoes to free carbon dioxide from carbonate rocks in large amounts (but it might have continued on a reduced scale: see Olympus Mons); and the frequency of meteor impacts diminished dramatically 3.8 billion years ago. The end of the cycle led to falling levels of carbon dioxide in the atmosphere. Without gaseous carbon dioxide, the greenhouse effect no longer functioned and, slowly but surely, Mars froze. If Venus can be characterized as having suffered a runaway greenhouse effect, then Mars underwent a runaway refrigerator effect.

It's different on Earth. Our vast reserves of interior heat are continually being renewed through radioactive decay deep in the core. This heat not only continues to support volcanoes, but the entire sea bed is regularly recycled through the mechanism of *plate tectonics*, in which heat from the planet's core causes the crust to recirculate in great plates. In this way, Earth's carbonate-silicate cycle continues and will continue for eons.

In addition, life reinforces the cycle on Earth. For the past 600 million years, marine organisms have been removing carbon dioxide from seawater to build their shells, which turn into limestone and chalk, eventually to become fodder for volcanoes.

Therefore, the main reason why Mars doesn't have a climate like that of Earth's 3.8 billion years ago is its size. There's every reason to believe that an Earth-sized planet at the orbit of Mars would have an atmosphere, oceans, and perhaps, just maybe, life.

Olympus Mons

It is improbable that Mars has remained volcanically active over 4 billion years only to lose volcanic activity over the last 200 million years.

Chris McKay, planetary scientist

Mars' Olympus Mons is the highest volcano in the solar system. With a summit about 16 miles above the surrounding surface, it's three times the height of Mount Everest, and at 360 miles across, it's the size of Oregon. The summit caldera, or central depression, is nearly two miles deep and 15 miles across.

Figure 4-8 shows an oblique view of Olympus Mons, created by stereoscopically processing several photographs taken by the Viking orbiters. Compare this oblique view with the vertical color image in C-8. The size of Olympus Mons is shown in Fig. 4-9 in comparison to another huge volcano, Pele, on Jupiter's moon Io (see Jupiter and the Volcanoes of Io), and the volcanic Hawaiian Islands.

Volcanoes grow over "hot spots" of molten rock (magma) deep below the surface. On Earth, great crustal plates move slowly over the surface, so a volcano might no sooner (in geological time) form than it drifts away from the source of heat that created it in the first place. This is how the Hawaiian Island chain was formed. The location of the hot spot is relatively unchanged, while the Pacific plate moves slowly over it at a rate of an inch or so per year. The result is graphically seen in any map of the islands: Kauai, Oahu, Molokai, Maui and Hawaii were all created in turn, Kauai being the oldest and Hawaii, with its great shield volcanoes of Mauna Loa and Mauna Kea, the youngest. (The hot spot is now south, rather than southeast, of Hawaii, indicating that the Pacific Plate has changed direction since the Kilauea complex was formed.)

Mars is too small to maintain the heat necessary to drive plate movements, so Olympus Mons just grew and grew only so long as deep source rock was hot enough to force basaltic magma to the surface. You can think of Olympus Mons (in paleontologist Stephen Jay Gould's phrase) as "all the Hawaii's, piled one atop the other." After the period of heavy meteorite bombardment had ended, about 3.8 bil-

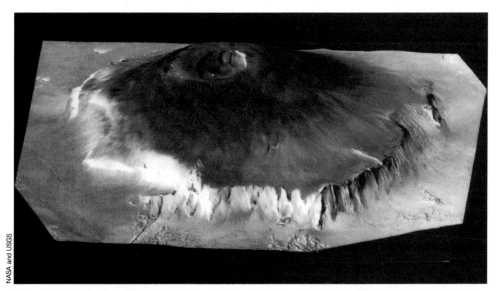

4-8 Mars' Olympus Mons, oblique view, in which you can see the 4 mile high scarp at the base of the volcano. See also C-8.

lion years ago, the Martian volcanoes were the only means by which carbon dioxide could be recycled back to the surface and into the atmosphere. For a while—perhaps hundreds of millions of years—whole atmospheres of carbon dioxide and oceans of water vapor poured from those great peaks.

Mars, however, was radiating heat at a profuse rate and, inevitably, the volcanoes died. The carbonate-silicate cycle (see *Mars: Nearly a living planet*) virtually ceased, the greenhouse effect broke down in the absence of atmospheric carbon dioxide, and the surface temperature dropped. As we have seen, Mars froze.

Today, volcanic activity on Mars no longer plays a role in controlling the planet's environment. Has it ceased completely? We're not sure. Take another look at C-8. Note the meteor craters on the flanks of the volcano. Planetary scientists use such craters to estimate the age of features, but here, with only a handful to be expected anyway, there isn't much of a database to form an opinion.

Let's assume the best: few visible craters mean that older craters are buried beneath lava flows, so perhaps we're seeing evidence of quite recent flows from the caldera at the summit. How recent? Prudent researchers talk in terms of "the last one-and-a-half billion years," while others optimistically put that figure at less than 100 million years. I hope the younger figure is the case: warm volcanoes could mean hydrothermal activity, (liquid water), which could in turn support some sort of anaerobic (living without air) life. Hope springs eternal in the search for life on Mars!

There are two more pieces of evidence (sort of) to support geologically recent volcanism on Mars. One is the finding of possible volcanic vents in the Valles Marineris of recent origin, "no older than a few million years and possibly less than 10 to 100 years," according to one optimistic scientist. The other relates to a

VOLCANOES COMPARED

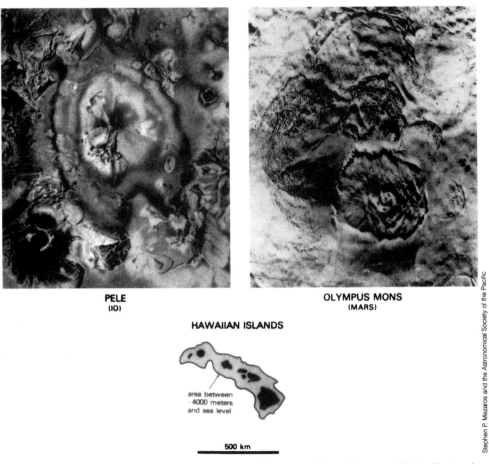

PELE
(IO)

OLYMPUS MONS
(MARS)

HAWAIIAN ISLANDS

area between
-4000 meters
and sea level

500 km

Stephen P. Mezaros and the Astronomical Society of the Pacific

4-9   Great volcanoes compared: Hawaii (Earth), Olympus Mons (Mars) and Pele (Jupiter's moon Io). The Hawaiian Island chain is one of the largest volcanic features on Earth. Slow northwest movement (plate tectonics) of the Earth's crust over a "hot spot" has created a succession of shield volcanoes, the islands. The hot spot is currently south of the "Big Island" of Hawaii. In the absence of plate tectonics on Mars, Olympus Mons just grew and grew.

story about a handful of meteorites known as *SNCs* (pronounced snicks) believed to have originated on Mars (see *Meteorites from Mars?*). One of these is estimated to have formed less than 400 million years ago, and it's definitely of volcanic origin.

All this might sound like pretty thin support for the notion that volcanoes were active on Mars comparatively recently, but it's probably the best we can do until we return to the planet. Super-high resolution photographs from the proposed

"Mars Observer" mission will certainly help, but it's going to take the return of samples from the Martian surface (initially by robot spacecraft) before most planetary scientists would be convinced there's still any appreciable warmth left in Mars. Then again, a photo of a fresh lava flow down the flanks of Olympus Mons would be pretty convincing, unlikely as we are to see it!

Life on Mars: Past, present and future

How can people say that nothing could have survived the Martian cold? Mars has not gone through any more dramatic changes inimical to life than the Earth has. For example, when that ultimate poison, oxygen, appeared, life managed to hold on here.

Gil Levin, designer and principal investigator of one of the Viking biology experiments

The past

We've seen how Mars once had a carbon dioxide-rich atmosphere and a surface at least partially covered by liquid water, quite similar to conditions on early Earth. Did life start on Mars about the time it began on Earth, only to die out when the planet froze and liquid water disappeared?

Possibly. The conditions were perfect, if Earth is anything to go by. About 3.8 billion years ago, the temperature on Mars was above freezing, the pressure was about what it was at the surface of Earth, and liquid water was abundant. There's a good chance Mars had great oceans, just as Earth (and perhaps Venus) had back then. The figure in C-8 shows how Mars might have looked, with a great ocean filling much of the northern hemisphere and intruding into Valles Marineris, much as the Mediterranean Sea is connected to the Atlantic. After carbon dioxide was no longer recycled into the atmosphere, the pressure and temperature dropped and deep oceans became ice-covered lakes. Life on Mars then might have resembled microbial mats found beneath ice-bound lakes of Antarctica.

By 3 million years ago, the only liquid water on Mars would have been found in rock pores, where microorganisms might have lived out their final generations. Eventually all liquid water disappeared from Mars and thus, again if Earth is a guide, life would have been extinguished. For all life on Earth needs the magic ingredient, liquid water.

The present

The two Viking landers (Figs. 4-10 and 4-11, C-9, and C-10) were equipped with exquisitely-sophisticated life-seeking laboratories. A mere cubic foot in size, each automated lab had the capacity to carry out three separate experiments, which between them would almost certainly have indicated the presence of carbon-based life.

Why do we look for life with a carbon base? For one reason, because it's the only kind we know, and because the carbon atom is remarkably gregarious. It practically cries out for company—in the form of other atoms—with which to make

NASA

4-10 Frost on Mars. This image was returned by Viking 2 on May 18, 1979. You can see a thin coating—probably no more than one thousandth of an inch thick—of water ice on the rocks and soil. When frost also appeared one Martian year (23 Earth months) previously, it lasted for about 100 days. The slope of the horizon is the result of Viking 2 landing with an eight degree tilt toward the west.

complex molecules. Carbon is flexible, it's able to make long chains, and it's hooked in such a way that it joins to itself and other atoms in limitless configurations. In short, it appears perfect as the foundation of life. This isn't to say that life *has* to be carbon-based, but for now it's hard to conceive of any other type.

Despite some ambiguities, most biologists concede that nothing was found in the data from the Viking landers to support the hope that life somehow survived on Mars—if it ever arose in the first place. This isn't to say life absolutely, definitely doesn't exist there. We only sampled in a couple of spots (it's a big planet after all, with a land area practically the same as Earth's), and we only sampled the surface. Perhaps, deep down, safe from the sun's deadly ultraviolet rays, some tough, tiny fellows have figured out how to live without liquid water in intensely cold, dark conditions. The odds have to be against it though (despite my blood-curdling movie memories of *War of the Worlds* and the original *Invaders from Mars*).

This is a high-stakes game when considering the likelihood of any extraterrestrial life. As astronomer Robert Jastrow pointed out in *Red Giants and White Dwarfs*, "If Martian life, or a fossilized trace of its past existence, is ever discovered, we will know that a long time ago nature conducted experiments on the origin of life on two planets, and on both planets the experiments succeeded. Therefore, the evolution of life out of nonlife cannot be an unlikely event."

The future

The technology for terraforming Mars, to turn it at least into the sort of place Earth *once* was—when life started here—already exists. If we really wanted to heat Mars and create an atmosphere and oceans of liquid water, we could. Using

NASA

4-11 The first panoramic view taken by Viking 1 from Mars. The top half abuts the bottom half for a nearly-complete 360 degree view. The horizon is approximately two miles away. Notice the sand dune feature on the left, top. In the top photo, the out-of-focus spacecraft component towards left center is the housing for the sample arm, not yet deployed. In the bottom photo, upper right, is the high-gain dish antenna for direct communication between the lander and Earth.

present-day technology, Mars could support life within a few hundred years. *Life* in this context isn't you or me—we'd still need to carry our own supply of oxygen around with us. We're talking here about primitive life such as blue-green algae, Earth's only life for billions of years. Don't knock it—that algae transformed our carbon dioxide atmosphere into the air you're breathing now. Eventually, in thousands of years, it could do the same for Mars.

So how do we get from here to there, to a Mars where blue-green algae and its cousins thrive, where we could walk around in our shirt sleeves with little "rebreathers" and small tanks of oxygen on our backs? In short, how could we turn the clock back, and create a Mars today like the Mars of billions of years ago, before carbon dioxide stopped recycling and the planet froze? Read on.

Terraforming Mars

No one knows how long it would take to complete the climate transformation of Mars—3,000 years or 100,000 years. Long before this comes to pass, however, people will be living on Mars and becoming Martians. Their histories may record that it all began in the final years of the twentieth century.

John Noble Wilford, Mars Beckons

As we've seen, the first step to terraforming Mars (that is, turning it from a cold dry planet into one on which we could live) is to inject "greenhouse gases" into the atmosphere. Let's see what's involved.

Plenty of sunlight reaches Mars' surface now. The problem is that most of the heat energy is reflected straight back into space. Greenhouse gases keep the heat in, so one obvious scenario is to recover carbon dioxide from the rocks (where we think there's plenty) and water vapor from the permafrost (if it's there) and from the poles (where we're sure there's water-ice). We'd be better off, though, using a more efficient greenhouse gas than carbon dioxide, such as the commonplace Freon in your refrigerator. Ironically, this gas, which causes intense damage to Earth's ozone layer, might ultimately be the key to recreating Mars' early climate.

OK, so we build great Freon-pumping factories on Mars, where the raw constituents of the gas can be found in surface rocks. All the technology for doing this exists today: we've sent humans to the moon, we've landed on Mars, and we know how to make huge quantities of chloroflourocarbon gases like Freon. Depending on whose model you believe, it might not take a great amount of an efficient greenhouse gas to turn the climate around (especially if you somehow sped things up by using sunlight to melt the polar ice caps), to introduce liquid water into the atmosphere, and thus create weather for the first time in 3 billion or so years. As temperatures increased, rock-bound carbon dioxide would be released, adding its contribution to the greenhouse effect. Best of all, perhaps, subsurface water should gush forth.

Water, water everywhere . . .

The little moisture Mars already has in its thin atmosphere is barely enough to coat the surface with a thin layer of ice (Fig. 4-10). However, we're fairly sure that Mars has vast underground reservoirs of frozen water—permafrost—perhaps thousands of feet thick. As the surface temperature rose, heat would begin to thaw the ice, releasing water, oceans of it. Simultaneously, water ice at the poles would melt, adding to the flow. Eventually, perhaps after a couple of hundred years, with seas of liquid water and a carbon dioxide atmosphere, Mars could support microorganisms.

At that point, you'd have something similar to early Earth, and our grandchildren's grandchildren would probably be thinking in terms of *true* terraforming: creating an atmosphere that they could breath. How do you turn a carbon dioxide-rich atmosphere into one like we have on Earth today? What you need is another sort of factory. Using sunlight as its energy source, it would convert carbon dioxide into oxygen, and it would (of course) be self-healing and self-replicating. Does that sound familiar?

Look outside. We're surrounded by such factories. We call them plants. Some of them (blue-green algae, for instance) thrive in an atmosphere consisting of nothing but carbon dioxide. Most other plants need at least a little oxygen, but the principle is the same: plants that once transformed Earth's atmosphere could do the same on Mars. It might take tens of thousands of years, but by careful choice of species and with a little cultivation, Mars could one day be a new pollution-free Garden of Eden.

Maybe we're attacking the problem from the wrong point of view, however. I end with this "lateral thought" from Freeman Dyson: "Now that genetic engineering is rapidly becoming a practical proposition, it is not absurd to think of redesigning terrestrial creatures so as to make them viable in space or on other celestial bodies." (from *Infinite in All Directions*). Perhaps it's not Mars that we should be terraforming, but us that we should be Martianizing.

Martian floods

The scenes [of Kasei Vallis] don't look markedly different from scenes throughout the American Southwest. Mesas and arroyos tell of a desert climate, and the streamlined bars and striations in the channel beds point unmistakably to occasional heavy erosion by water.

Mark Robinson, *Astronomy*, October 1989

We're virtually certain liquid water once flowed on Mars, and we also believe Mars still has immense quantities of this water frozen below the surface in the form of permafrost. One confirming piece of evidence is the gigantic size of flood channels photographed by the Viking orbiters.

The orbiters weren't equipped with what are currently the best instruments for obtaining data on surface topography: radar altimeters. However, some areas *were* recorded stereoscopically, that is, with two or more photographs taken from different positions. Using mapping techniques developed for Earthly terrain, the United States Geological Survey was able to produce detailed contour maps of parts of Mars. Kasei Vallis (valley) is one of these areas.

To locate Kasei Vallis, let's start with one of the largest features on Mars, Valles Marineris. This huge rift valley (as long as the United States is wide and in places as deep as Mount Everest is high) runs quarter-way around the Martian equator. (It's named after the Mariner series of probes, which sent back our first photographs of Mars, starting with Mariner 4 in November, 1964.) Northwest of Valles Marineris is volcano-studded Tharsis Ridge with Olympus Mons beyond (on the northwest edge of the ridge), the biggest and highest volcano of the solar system. North of the east section of Valles Marineris lies Chryse Planitia, Schiaparelli's "Plain of Gold." That's now home to Viking 1, no longer working, a future museum treasure for generations to come.

Bird's eye views

Between Olympus Mons and Chryse Planitia lies Kasei Vallis, an immense flood-channel system 1,500 miles long and up to 200 miles wide. (Kasei means "Mars" in Japanese.) The flood that deluged this part of Mars a billion or so years ago left scars unmatched by Earthly standards. By using the stereoscopic images and subsequent contour mapping to produce bird's eye views of the valley, we can imagine what it would be like to soar over it, and we can visualize the wild flood that created it.

Figure 4-12 shows part of the great flood-carved south branch of Kasei Vallis in a vertical view taken by the Viking 1 orbiter. You can get a sense of the size of the channels from the crater at the bend, which is about 80 miles in diameter (compare that to Meteor Crater, Arizona, a mere four-fifths of a mile across, Fig. 6-1).

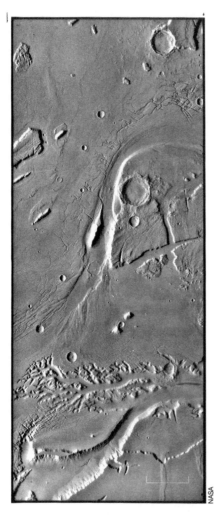

4-12   Kasei Vallis as imaged by the Viking orbiters, north at the top. The scale bar at the bottom is 200 kilometers (about 124 miles) long. Notice where the flow (from southwest to northeast) appears to have overshot the channel at the bend, and the teardrop-shaped island, typical of flood features on Earth. Figure 4-13 imagines you to be 25,000 feet above the bottom left corner of this image, looking towards the northeast (i.e., up and to the right).

Now imagine flying 25,000 feet above the valley, looking northeast. You'd see something like the computer-generated view in Fig. 4-13, in which the vertical scale has been exaggerated for clarity. Once, one quarter of a cubic mile per second of water created this valley in its headlong rush. It's impossible for us to comprehend such a cataclysmic flood. The only comparable (but much smaller) feature on Earth, produced from less than a tenth of this flow, is the Channeled Scablands in eastern Washington state.

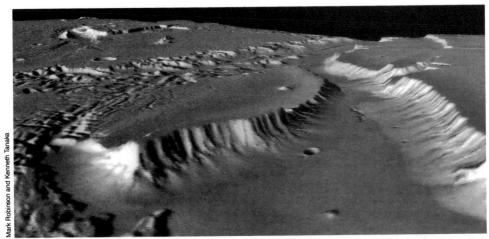

4-13   The southern branch of Kasei Vallis. The maximum relief from the deepest point in the channel (center background) to the upper reaches of Lunae Planum (right middle) is over 10,000 feet. In the left background, the main northern branch of Kasei Vallis can be seen making a sharp eastward turn. The viewpoint for this image is the lower left corner of Fig. 4-12, looking northeast from about 25,000 feet above ground. The vertical scale has been exaggerated by a factor of two.

Where did the water come from? What caused the flood? Mars almost certainly had an arid climate at the time, so the water presumably originated in the Martian crust, in one or more frozen aquifers of permafrost. What caused the breakout? One guess is that a great meteorite crashed into Mars, rupturing the surface and melting great quantities of ice below. The water poured out, as if from a broken dam, and Kasei Vallis was the result.

This scenario certainly gives hope to would-be terraformers who pin their hopes on whole oceans of water being stored, as permafrost, just below the dusty Martian surface.

Martian miscellany

Mars rules catastrophes and war, it is master of the daylight hours of Tuesday and the hours of darkness on Friday . . . being of choleric temper it especially rules males between the ages of 42 and 57.

Fifteenth century German manuscript

- It seems Mars has always had a bad reputation. An ancient Babylonian cuneiform tablet states, "When Nergal (Mars) is dim, it is lucky; when bright, unlucky."

- The symbol for Mars (and, for our sins, the male sex) is a shield and spear.

- The Norse name for Mars is Tui, hence our word Tuesday. In Romance languages, the Latin "Mars" is used, so Tuesday is Mardi (French), martes (Spanish) and martedì (Italian).

- The total area of Mars is about that of Earth's land area.

- The famous "canals" of Mars were first seen in 1877 by Giovanni Schiaparelli, uncle of renowned Parisian couturier, Elsa Schiaparelli.

- In Italian, the primary meaning of the word *canali* is channels, which is probably what Schiaparelli meant to describe. The secondary meaning *canals* (implying the presence of intelligent inhabitants) was picked up by the press in the U.S. According to Carl Sagan, "The whole hypothesis [of life on Mars] was right there in the translation."

- Canals or channels, a wealthy Bostonian named Percival Lowell abandoned his Oriental studies to search for them, and he built the Flagstaff Observatory in Arizona for this purpose.

- Lowell "saw" the lines, but other observers put them down to the tendency of humans to try to "connect the dots" (just like we do with constellations). In this case, the dots were fuzzy splotches on the surface.

- One of the first subjects studied by California's Lick Observatory when it opened 100 years ago was the Martian "canal network." (One observer, John Schaeberle, thought he saw them, but other, more experienced observers couldn't make them out.)

- In 1938, Orson Welles transposed the site of the H.G. Wells, 1897 novel "The War of the Worlds" from southern England to the eastern U.S., scaring many people with the radio play in which Martian invaders overwhelmed Earthly defenses.

- Even with the naked eye, you can't help noticing that Mars is orange, and it's even more noticeable through binoculars or a telescope. Why? Because the Martian surface is about 13% iron. That's rust you're looking at.

- Viking I landed on June 20, 1976, on a plain named a century earlier by Schiaparelli. The place was called *Chryse Planitia*, or "plain of gold" in Greek. Neither gold nor life was found, despite three cunningly-designed experiments.

- Trivia question: What does KVUGNG mean? Answer: Nothing to us, everything to Viking. It was the code word transmitted to the Viking I orbiter on July 29, 1976, ordering release of the lander. A few hours later it transmitted TV pictures back from the surface.

- Mars' two moons, Phobos (Fear) and Deimos (Flight), are probably captured asteroids. In mythology, they're the attendants of Mars according to

Homer's Iliad. In reality, they're tiny (14 and 7 miles across, respectively) and irregularly shaped bodies, too small for their gravities to have pulled them into spheres.

- Phobos is the only known moon to circle its parent planet in less time than the planet takes to revolve on its own axis. Seen from Mars, only 6,000 miles away, Phobos rises in the west and sets in the east. It would appear to be about one quarter the diameter our moon appears to us.

- The Viking landers were designed to last for only a few months after reaching the Martian surface. They both exceeded expectations: Viking 2 lasted until 1980, while Viking I sent back its last picture on November 5, 1982.

- Swimming is one sport that would feel the same on Mars as on Earth. In most other sports athletes fight gravity, whereas a swimmer fights viscosity. Gravity on Mars is thirty-eight percent of what it is here, but the viscosity of water is the same.

Venus: Not your average vacation paradise

Before the Space Age, Venus was widely regarded as a potential colony. Now, we have to resign ourselves to the fact that it is as hostile as it could possibly be.

Gary Hunt and Patrick Moore, *The Planet Venus*.

Venus is not your regular holiday resort. Its surface is, you might say, "hotter'n hell," about 900 degrees Fahrenheit. The pressure there is nothing to envy either; it's about what you'd feel if you dove about half a mile down into one of Earth's oceans. There is no liquid water on Venus. If there was, it would boil away before you could say Ishtar (the Babylonian name for the planet, meaning "bright torch of heaven"). And if you managed to survive the heat and pressure, you'd still be eaten by sulphuric acid in the atmosphere.

In spite of these daunting conditions, we've seen the surface of Venus, via television pictures returned by robot probes, and in particular from the series of Soviet "Venera" landers. A handful survived on the surface for an hour or more before their electronics were fried—just enough time to send back images of stark, rock-strewn plains and plateaus (Fig. 4-14) under a bright orange sky. Near-instant analysis of the soil told us that the landers were sitting on volcanic basalt, and we now believe virtually all the surface of Venus is volcanic.

Through a telescope, Venus appears a faint yellow color, suggesting that Venusian clouds aren't made of water vapor like Earth's white clouds. They consist mainly of droplets of sulphuric acid swirling around in a thick carbon dioxide-rich atmosphere; see Fig. 4-15. This ugly combination makes it impossible to see the surface of the planet from above, so we have to resort to radar.

Seeing by radar

On May 4, 1989, astronauts in the space shuttle Atlantis carefully launched the space probe they had just carried into Earth's orbit. The probe, named *Magellan*

ВЕНЕРА-14 ОБРАБОТКА ИППИ АН СССР И ЦДКС

ВЕНЕРА-14 ОБРАБОТКА ИППИ АН СССР И ЦДКС

4-14 Two images sent back to Earth from the Soviet Venera 14 lander in its short lifetime on the surface of Venus, March 1982. Soil analyses found basalts similar to those found on the seabed of Earth.

after the Portuguese circumnavigator, arrived at its destination a few months later and has been in orbit around Venus ever since.

Before Magellan began its detailed plot of the surface of Venus in the fall of 1990, we had a rough idea of the planet's topography from low-resolution sources: Soviet and U.S. orbiters, equipped with radar altimeters; and the giant Arecibo, Puerto Rico, radio telescope (Fig. 4-16), which was used as a radar transmitter and receiver—an astonishing feat, considering we never get closer than 24 million miles to Venus. See Frank Drake's foreword.

NASA's Magellan spacecraft is a triumph of technology. It uses high-resolution side-scanning radar to produce finely-detailed images by beaming down powerful signals that bounce back from the planet's hidden surface. The timing and "pattern" of the echo, when received by Magellan and radioed back to Earth, are raw data for mapping the topography and surface texture of Venus. The images can also be used to produce three-dimensional views of the planet's surface, such as that in Fig. 4-17. This is a synthetic view of the 20-mile diameter meteor crater Golubkina.

You can see Golubkina's terraced inner walls and a central peak. Such a peak, typical of those found in impact craters on bodies as different and far apart as Earth and Saturn's moon Mimas (Figs. 6-2, 6-5), forms when the inner crater floor rebounds immediately after the impact. Figure 4-18, also of Golubkina, is a mosaic produced for comparison from data obtained from Magellan in 1990 and from Soviet "Venera" spacecraft six years earlier. Magellan's resolution is about ten times that of the Venera orbiters.

Although Golubkina might be as much as 400 million years old, notice how sharp the features appear. Fresh craters on Earth are quickly eroded by water and

NASA

4-15 Venus imaged in ultraviolet light. While the solid body of the planet takes 243 days to revolve, the cloud tops seen here whirl around in a mere 4 days. The energy for motion of the clouds appears to come from solar energy, which is absorbed and converted to heat in the upper atmosphere.

ice. On arid Venus, however, erosion from wind and chemical erosion from the corrosive atmosphere happens much more slowly, adding to the difficulty of dating such a crater.

We have a pretty fair idea of what Venus is like now. We also can infer what it might have been like long ago, when the planet probably lived a little better up to its namesake, the goddess of love and beauty.

SETI Institute and Frank Drake

4-16   Much of our pre-Magellan (1989) knowledge of the surface of Venus came from radar mapping of the planet by the 1,000 ft. diameter Arecibo radio telescope, a giant steel web strung across a valley in Puerto Rico. Originally designed for military use (detection of Soviet missile launches), it was readily adapted to both conventional radio astronomy and for radar mapping of comparatively nearby objects. At its re-dedication in 1974, a signal was transmitted in the direction M13, a large globular cluster of stars in Hercules, telling "them" something about us. (If they reply immediately upon receipt, we should hear in about 50,000 years.)

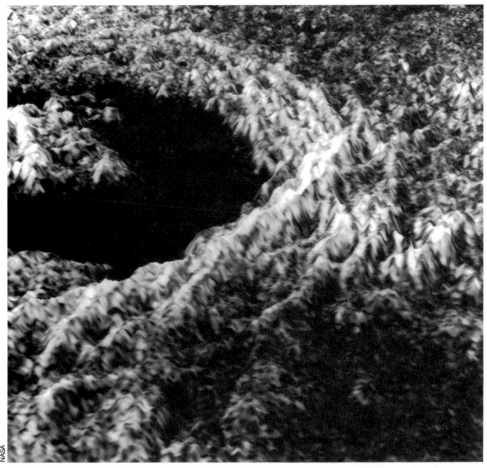

NASA

4-17 Golubkina meteor crater, as imaged by the the U.S. Magellan orbiter in summer, 1990. Magellan's high-resolution side-scanning radar provided data to create this 3-dimensional view of the 20-mile diameter crater. Note particularly the central peak, typical of many impact craters seen on Earth, Mars, and many moons. It's caused by the rebounding of the inner floor after impact. Almost all of Venus' features are named after women. Anna Golubkina (1864-1927) was a Russian sculptress.

Good old Venus

Might waves have once rolled across the planet to crash on the shores of Ishtar? Did streams scour the flanks of Beta Regio?

R. Stephen Saunders, project scientist for the Magellan mission.
[Ishtar and Beta Regio are topographic features on Venus.]

The surface of Venus is a barren, desolate hothouse. Photographs sent back from the landers of the Soviet Venera during their brief lives on the surface show slablike rocks of volcanic basalt and a little soil under a bright orange sky. In many ways, the surface resembles the floor of a dried-up ocean. The question is, is it?

NASA

4-18 Magellan versus Venera. Golubkina crater is shown in a radar-produced mosaic. Top-left, as imaged by Magellan in 1990, and bottom-right, by the Soviet Venera 15 and 16 orbiters in 1983-84. The Soviet data have a resolution of about one mile, whereas data from the more-advanced Magellan radar have a resolution of about 400 feet.

Venus today is a very different place from Venus of 3 or 4 billion years ago. We have good reason to believe Venus and Earth were quite similar then, but whereas the climate on Earth remained relatively stable, that on Venus was changed irrevocably. Once again, carbon dioxide was the key. Even though the two planets have about the same amount of the gas today, on Earth it's mostly locked up in rocks, while on Venus it's mainly in the atmosphere. The atmosphere of Venus is 97% carbon dioxide, while Earth's contains a mere 0.03% by volume. (Such a trivial fraction means that we can, and do, rapidly increase the relative carbon dioxide concentration by burning fossil fuels. See *The greenhouse effect.*)

About 4.6 billion years ago, Venus, Earth, and Mars accreted from similar material: condensate from a warm nebula of dusty gas surrounding the newly-switched on sun. The general consensus among researchers is that this material was very dry, because volatile materials (including water) would have boiled away before initial accretion. A secondary accretion followed in the form of a prolonged bombardment from dripping-wet "tarball" comets, which had formed in the outer solar system where the sun's influence wasn't strong enough to boil away volatiles. (This is known as the *inhomogenous accretion* model.)

Oceans on Venus?

We believe Earth acquired oceans of water as a result of volatile cometary material raining down from the skies, and we're pretty sure Mars did likewise. What about Venus? It's likely the planet initially acquired about as much water as Earth did because it's nearly the same size, exerts roughly the same gravitational pull (91% that of Earth), and it was in the same part of the solar system as Earth when we received our water. So what happened?

Scientists are divided on whether Venus actually had oceans or not. One view is that it was *always* too hot at the surface. Any water arriving at the surface via comets would have immediately been evaporated and lofted high into the atmosphere, where the molecules underwent "photodissociation," and the hydrogen was lost forever into space.

Another possibility is that once, between 3 and 4 billion years ago, the surface of Venus was cool enough for oceans of liquid water to exist, because although Venus receives about twice the intensity of solar energy Earth receives, the sun was 30% cooler 4 billion years ago. Over millions of years the sun got warmer until a critical point was reached, and the oceans boiled away in a runaway greenhouse effect.

With our knowledge of the surface of Venus, you'd think it would be easy to decide whether what we're seeing is ancient ocean beds. The problem is Venus has been repaved extensively—perhaps totally—with lava from volcanoes. Most of the present surface is less than a billion, and perhaps only 200 million, years old. It might require hardier spacecraft than the Veneras to land on Venus and take core samples, perhaps returning them to Earth for examination before we know for sure. Unlike Mars, where the water is still there, in the poles and possibly frozen underground, Venus' water is lost for all time. We can't bring it back.

All in all, it appears to be a hopeless case—which is probably why you don't hear a lot of talk about terraforming Venus these days.

5

The outer planets

The interior structures of Jupiter, Saturn, Uranus and Neptune . . . and the Sun are in large part variations on a single theme: a rotating sphere of hydrogen and helium gas.

Timothy Dowling, *Astronomy*, October 1990.

The solar system can be divided neatly into inner and outer regions. Each of the outer planets—Jupiter, Saturn, Uranus and Neptune—can be imagined as an Earth-like ball covered by an enormous blanket of gas consisting mainly of hydrogen and helium. You can compare their great size with that of Earth in Fig. 5-1. In overall composition, they're much closer to the sun's make-up than to any of the inner planets. Distant Pluto is an exception: no gas blanket, just a little icy ball two-thirds the size of our moon, perhaps with a very tenuous atmosphere.

You can get some sense of the scale of the outer solar system as compared with its inner region from a remarkable series of 60 photographs taken on Valentine's Day, 1990, when Voyager 1 looked back from nearly 4 billion miles from Earth. The spacecraft's trajectory past Saturn in 1980 had lobbed it out of the plane of the ecliptic (defined by Earth's orbit, and which approximates the orbital plane of the other planets except for Pluto), so it had a bird's eye view of the solar system. Using both wide-angle and narrow-angle cameras, Voyager created a unique family portrait (Fig. 5-2), in which six of the nine planets—including the four large outer planets—can be identified. Look for a long moment at the key diagram (Fig. 5-3) and try to imagine the remoteness of Voyager's vantage point. The 39-picture wide-angle mosaic is the most graphic demonstration I've seen of how lonely and empty the solar system actually is.

This section covers a few highlights of the outer solar system: Jupiter's volcanic moon Io; the rings of Saturn; Miranda, Uranus' little "inside-out" moon; and Triton, a chemistry laboratory of a moon orbiting Neptune. We'll also pause to admire Voyager 2, a venerable spacecraft that far exceeded the requirements of its original mission. Pluto is also acknowledged—briefly, because it's the only planet in the solar system not yet visited by a spacecraft from Earth, so our knowledge of the planet is very limited.

Stephen P. Mezaros and the Astronomical Society of the Pacific

5-1   Jupiter, Saturn, Uranus, and Neptune, the four "gas giants" of the solar system, compared with the size of Earth. Although the largest planet, Jupiter could hold 1,400 Earths, it still has far too little mass to become a star. A body with a mass of 10 Jupiters would be a "brown dwarf," a pseudostar. You'd need at least 80 Jupiters to get a full-blown star.

Twenty years ago, prior to our first visit to Jupiter (December 1973, Pioneer 10), the same could have been said about any of the outer planets. All that we knew had been gleaned from Earth-based observations, and that was precious little. Since then, four spacecraft have flown by Jupiter, three by Saturn, and one by Uranus and Neptune. Now, with budget cuts and the ever-present specter of canceled missions, the golden era that began with the 1969 manned moon landing might have come to an end. Whatever the eventual outcome of NASA's financial belt-tightening, the transformation of the outer planets, in less than two decades,

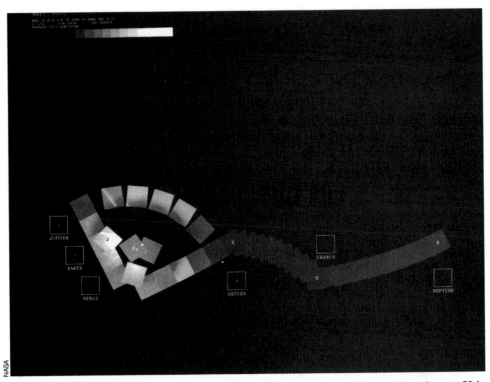

NASA

5-2   Voyager 1's historic mosaic of 39 wide-angle images of the solar system taken on Valentine's Day, 1990. At the time Voyager was high above the plane of the ecliptic (the orbital path of Earth, approximating that of the planets, except Pluto) and about 3.7 billion miles from Earth (or 40 times as far as Earth is from the sun). The mosaic was created by starting at Neptune, working in to Uranus and Saturn, passing horizontally below and to the left of the sun, arcing about and to the right of the sun, and finally jumping to the frames containing Mars. Our sun is the bright object in the center of the quarter-circle of frames. It's not as large as seen from Voyager, only about one fortieth of the diameter as seen from Earth, but is still millions of times brighter than the next brightest star. Scattered light in the pictures results from this great luminosity. The insets are magnifications from a further 21 narrow-angle photographs centered on the individual planets. The images of Uranus and Neptune are smeared due to spacecraft motion during the long (15-second) exposures. Three planets are not identified: Mercury was masked by the sun's glare, Mars was too small and dim to be positively identified, and Pluto was too small, dark and distant to be imaged.

from specks in the night sky to rainbow images of convoluted worlds, is rich achievement we can savor over and over again.

Jupiter and the volcanoes of Io

There remains the matter which seems to me . . . the most important in this work, namely, that I should disclose and publish to the world the

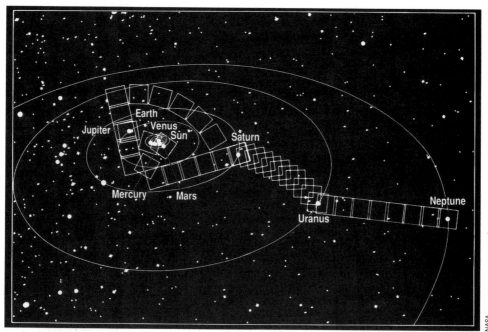

5-3 The diagram shows the planets' locations in their orbits at the time the images in Fig. 5-2 were taken.

occasion of discovering and observing four planets, never seen from the very beginning of the world up to our own times.

Galileo Galilei, *The Starry Messenger*, 1610

Jupiter is the largest planet in our solar system. It consists of a comparatively tiny rocky core enveloped by a thick blanket of dense metallic hydrogen, with tiers of thick hydrogen and helium gas in the atmosphere above. The outer skin (what we actually see) is a layer of multicolored clouds whose psychedelic complexity delighted scientists and nonscientists alike when the first close-up photographs of Jupiter were received from Pioneer 10 in 1973.

The most curious feature of this outer skin is Jupiter's Great Red Spot (seen in C-11), an immense vortex of cold clouds rotating counterclockwise at enormous velocity. At first glance, it looks something like a terrestrial hurricane as seen from an orbiting weather satellite. However, lacking a central "eye," with an age of at least 100 years, and with a diameter three times that of Earth, its mechanism seems to be much more complicated. We're not sure just how long it's been around: In 1664, English astronomer Robert Hooke reported that he'd seen, ". . . a spot in the largest of the three observed belts of Jupiter . . . Its diameter is one-tenth of Jupiter . . ." The spot later shrank and vanished, but then reappeared (or another appeared for the first time). We do know its appearance changes dramatically over time. For example, it's now about half the size it was at the beginning of this century.

Jupiter itself is about midway in volume between Earth and the sun: 1,400 Earths would fit into Jupiter, while 930 Jupiters would fit into the sun. You can get a feel for Jupiter's girth from Fig. 5-4, in which Earth has been superimposed next to the Great Red Spot.

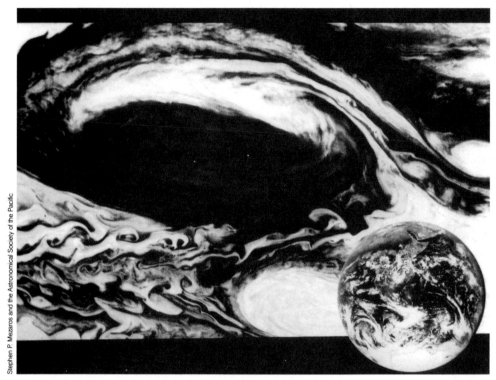

Stephen P. Mezaros and the Astronomical Society of the Pacific

5-4 The size of Earth compared with Jupiter's Great Red Spot. About three Earths would fit across the Spot, which has been closely observed for over a century. It might be the same feature noted by Robert Hooke in 1664.

The Jovian system is a minisolar system in its own right, with at least 16 satellites. Of these, four (Io, Europa, Callisto, and Ganymede) have been known and observed since Galileo discovered them in 1610. One of them in particular would surely make anyone's *Seven Wonders of the Solar System* list: Io and its sulfur volcanoes.

A mad painter's palette

Io (EYE-oh) is about the size of our moon. In C-11, where Io is in front of the Great Red Spot, one glance at its bright orange color tells you there's something curious going on. A closer view (C-12) of the "pepperoni pizza moon" looks like some mad painter's palette of red, orange and yellow lava flows. Stranger yet is the volcanic eruption seen on the limb of the moon. (The brightness of the plume has been artificially enhanced, but the actual color has been preserved.) The 100-mile high eruption requires an ejection velocity of 1,500 mph, half that of a speeding bullet. The source of the plume has been identified as a volcanic structure now named *Pele* after the fiery goddess of Hawaii's Kilauea.

How can such a relatively small body maintain active volcanoes? Why isn't Io geologically dead, like our moon? Otherwise the two have much in common. They're about the same size and density, they both orbit their parent planets at about the same distance, and they both keep the same hemisphere facing towards their planets in synchronous rotation. The smaller a body is, the faster it loses heat generated by the decay of radioactive isotopes, and in the case of our moon, lava flows ceased over 3 billion years ago. Yet here's Io with no craters, very recent lava flows covering its surface, and active volcanoes spewing out plumes of sulfur at huge velocities. What's going on here?

The real surprise is that Io's volcanism *wasn't* a total surprise. Just days before Voyager 1 took the first detailed photographs of Io in March, 1979, scientists from the University of California and NASA predicted that something of the kind would be found. They calculated the tidal-stretching forces resulting from Io's very close, somewhat elliptical, orbit around massive Jupiter, and showed that these would cause a great outpouring of heat. (In contrast, Earth, with a small fraction of Jupiter's mass, has a relatively tiny heating effect on our moon.) The mechanism still isn't fully understood, because tidal friction might not account for all the heat generated: internal radioactivity might play a role, and Io's interaction with Jupiter's magnetic field could also be involved.

What we do know is that Io is constantly turning its crustal skin inside out, and the mottled surface we now see has been recycled many times in the moon's history. The absence of impact craters on Io tells us that the surface is very young geologically. Every century, an average of four inches of volcanic debris is spread on the surface. In Earthly terms, an equivalent volume to that ejected by Mount St. Helens in May 1980 erupts every month from Io's volcanoes.

Pele is shown in C-13. The plume of its geyser-like eruption rises nearly 200 miles above the surface. Notice the concentric rings of yellow and brown deposits from the volcano. Pele's eruptions are apparently intermittent, because it was quiet four months later when Voyager 2 arrived at Jupiter.

In November 1995, NASA's long-delayed Galileo spacecraft will reach Jupiter after a complicated trajectory taking it once past Venus and twice past Earth. High on the list of "must-see" objects is Io. With luck (a great deal, because as I write this Galileo's deep space communication antenna is stuck closed), we'll then be able to better decipher this complex, intriguing world first seen by Galileo Galilei nearly 400 years ago.

The rings of Saturn

The planet Saturn is not one alone, but is composed of three, which almost touch one another and never move nor change with respect to one another . . . the middle one is about three times the size of the lateral ones.

Galileo Galilei, *The Starry Messenger*, 1610.

What occasioned this misrepresentation of Saturn by Galileo during the world's first telescopic inspection of the planet? Surely Saturn *is* "one alone," the second largest planet in the solar system (after Jupiter), a vast sphere composed mainly of hydrogen and helium. It's been known since people first looked at the night sky, because at its brightest only two stars outshine the planet.

Until Galileo focused one of the first "optick sticks" (telescopes) on Saturn, there was no reason to suspect it was very different in appearance from any of the other planets. So the observation by the obscure mathematics teacher, of "three, which almost touch each other," must have caused some cynicism in the streets of Padua. I imagine the scoffers had another field day two years later, in 1612, when he wrote, "the attendant bodies have disappeared. Are the two lesser stars consumed after the manner of solar spots? Has Saturn, perhaps, devoured his own children? The unexpected nature of the event, the weakness of my understanding, and the fear of being mistaken, have greatly confounded me."

As well they might. In retrospect, we can follow exactly what was going on. Unknown to Galileo, Saturn has a bright ring system that encircles the planet's equator. Like Earth, Saturn's spin isn't perfectly perpendicular to its orbit, tilting 28 degrees compared to our 23. So as Saturn moves in its 29-year journey around the sun, we see the inclination of the rings varying alternately from edge-on to a maximum of 28 degrees. The process is equivalent to the process that gives us our seasons. If you were on the sun (asbestos-clad) and Earth had rings circling the equator, they'd be prominent at the solstices and virtually invisible at the equinoxes.

At their maximum tilt, Saturn's rings are very prominent for two reasons: they reflect sunlight very well (they have a high *albedo*); and they're huge, with a diameter about two-thirds that of the distance between Earth and the moon. When they're edge-on to us, however, they're essentially invisible because they are thin. (Imagine tilting a Frisbee back and forth.)

Back to Galileo. In 1610, the rings were approaching their edge-on appearance: still visible, but getting less so. Seen through his modest telescope (with only about thirty-times magnification), Saturn appeared as one big body with a smaller body on each side. We have more than Galileo's words to go by: a letter dated July 10, 1610, containing his sketch of Saturn, survives (Fig. 5-5). Two years later the rings were edge-on, and therefore invisible. It wasn't until 1659 that Dutch astronomer (and inventor of the pendulum clock) Christiaan Huygens, using a fifty-power telescope, proposed the true explanation.

The world had to wait a little longer for a detailed view. Pioneer 11 took the first close-up photographs of Saturn's rings in 1979, and even higher resolution pictures arrived from Voyagers 1 and 2 in 1980–81. The images were both delightful and baffling (Fig. 5-6). Far from the handful of rings seen previously through Earthbound telescopes, the two Voyagers saw *thousands* of separate rings (C-14) consisting of countless individual particles. We saw not just quantity, but a great variety. Different rings are made up of different sized particles, from icy blocks up to a hundred feet across down to tiny grains of dust. Some rings are opaque, some are transparent.

Although Saturn's rings aren't unique (Jupiter, Uranus, and Neptune all have loᴛᴇ in fila seeſdo la lũghᴇʳᵛᴀ

o quella ꝺi meⱬⱬo, aᴉⱱᴇᴀ g. ⱱ

altre . ⱬ . Cateᴛali, eᴛ ꜱtanno

ꞏ forma . ○○○ . ꜱi come g

ⱱedeᴛe à loᴛo Aﹾﻴⁱᵉ eⱬſendo in

uᴛ bellᴵᵗ̃ᵐ̃ᵃ comoꝺᴉᵗa̓ ꝺᴉ · oᴛᴛᴇᴛ

5-5 Extract from a letter of Galileo's dated July 30, 1610, with a sketch of Saturn, "composed of three, which almost touch one another."

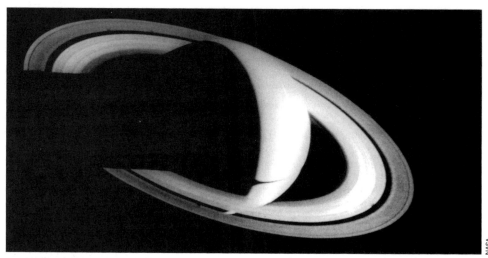

5-6 Saturn from Voyager, in a view we never get from Earth. Because we're so close—from Saturn's point of view—to the sun, we only get to see the entire sunlit side of the planet. Here, Voyager 1, having flown past, is now seeing the unlit "backside." Notice how abruptly the planet's shadow cuts sunlight off from the rings. This photograph was taken by Voyager 1 on November 16, 1980, at a distance of about 3 million miles from the planet. You could stuff nearly a thousand Earths into Saturn, while the diameter of the rings is more than halfway of Earth's distance from the moon.

thin rings), they're a major puzzle in their own right. How were they formed? Why are there so many? Are they permanent? If we find other planetary systems, should we expect to find rings there too? Questions abound, but the best guesses so far, like the rings seen edge-on, appear pretty thin.

NASA's proposed Cassini mission, with a 36-orbit examination of Saturn and its moons and rings, should change that. The mission also calls for a probe to be dropped into the hazy atmosphere of Saturn's largest moon, Titan. (The probe is named Huygens, after the seventeenth century Dutch astronomer who discovered the moon.) Assuming sufficient funding for the mission, Cassini should be launched in April 1996 for a rendezvous with Saturn in December 2002, over 20 years after our last visit to the ringed planet.

Uranus and its inside-out moon

Holy Moly! Is this for real?

Laurence Soderblom, geologist, on his first look at Miranda via Voyager 2

Uranus and Neptune are twins under the surface. Each is believed to have a rocky core approximately ten times the mass of Earth, covered by a thick mantle of liquid water, methane, and ammonia, and an immense atmosphere of hydrogen and helium gas. As seen by Voyager 2, the similarity isn't so obvious. They are both predominantly pale blue, indicating the presence of methane gas, which absorbs the red and reflects the blue end of the spectrum. However, Uranus is virtually featureless, a blue blob, while the top of Neptune's atmosphere is full of interesting features, such as clouds and oval storm systems.

This is odd, isn't it? You'd think the nearer a planet was to the sun, the more activity you'd see. For instance, Jupiter has a much more intense and colorful atmosphere than Saturn because it's closer to the sun and receives about three times as much solar energy over the same area. This translates into a more dynamic atmosphere, with resulting phenomena like storm systems (e.g., the Great Red Spot). The additional heat also allows organic chemicals to synthesize more readily on Jupiter, so it's more colorful. Jupiter and Saturn also have considerable internal heat sources, but they're roughly equivalent. They both radiate about 1.6 times as much energy as they would if they depended entirely on what they receive from the sun.

Similarly, you'd expect Uranus, which is fifty percent closer to the sun (at 19 AU), to have more diverse atmospheric features than Neptune (30 AU); however, the reverse is true. Of the four gas giants, Uranus is the odd man out. The reason lies in its small internal heat source. While at least forty percent of the heat emitted by Jupiter, Saturn, and Neptune comes from inside the planets, the figure for Uranus is less than six percent. This results in an anomalous situation: Neptune orbits a billion miles farther from the sun than Uranus, yet they each have the same temperature (about minus 350 degrees F). Internal heat, it seems, is just what Neptune needs to drive its atmosphere; lack of it leaves Uranus looking bland.

For the amateur astronomer, Uranus does have one advantage over Neptune: you can see it (just!) with your naked eye. Had it been much brighter, we can be sure that ancient sky-watchers would have identified it as a planet (the word comes from "wanderer" in ancient Greek, i.e., planets wander through the fixed background stars). Because it is pretty faint, no one paid Uranus any particular attention. Ironically, it was listed as a star before discovery in 1781, when German-English musician-astronomer William Hershel identified it as a planet. Then we had to wait until 1986 for Voyager 2's brief fly-by to get a close look. Given its featureless appearance, this hardly seemed to warrant the effort. But then we lucked out, when Voyager turned its cameras on Miranda.

A bizarre hybrid

Miranda is arguably the strangest body in the solar system. Its surface is simultaneously young and old, smooth and rough, jumbled and homogeneous. One of Uranus' 15 known moons, Miranda, is only 300 miles across. (Of the other moons, four are larger and the rest much smaller, less than 100 miles across).

It just happened that Miranda was perfectly placed for Voyager 2 to get a close look at it during the Uranus fly-by on January 24, 1986. In addition, Voyager's engineers had made considerable modifications to its computer software while en route from Saturn, resulting in much clearer photographs than we'd have otherwise received (see *The flight of Voyager 2*).

Scientists knew something was odd about Miranda when they received the first distant, fuzzy photograph (Fig. 5-7). As Voyager got closer, the resolution of the photos improved and the final computer-processed images (Figs. 5-8, 5-9 and C-15) were almost unbelievable. We had come to believe that any self-respecting body the size of Miranda would be perfectly round, with a basic smoothness modified only by 4 billion year old impact craters. Since that time, other than the odd meteor impact, it should have remained dead and cold. The little internal heat it once had would have radiated to space long ago. We certainly wouldn't expect to find signs of any dynamic processes.

What caused this wild jumbled landscape (like "scoops of marble-fudge ice cream"), which showed far fewer impact craters than we'd expect? The best guess of planetary scientists is that we're not looking at the original Miranda, which presumably accreted with the rest of the solar system 4½ billion years ago, but at a "new, improved" version of Miranda, which assembled more recently.

When a planet or moon first forms, the densest material migrates to the core while the lightest material ends up on the surface, in a process known as *differentiation*. The usual assumption is that some time after Miranda had differentiated, it was fragmented, perhaps because it strayed too close to the gravitational field of Uranus and was torn apart by tidal forces. The pieces eventually reassembled, but now what was once the dense core ended up partially on the outside, while some of the original surface is now in the core, a case of turning inside-out. The process might even have happened several times, resulting in great chunks of material apparently sticking out at random from the surface. The early history of meteor impacts has been lost forever.

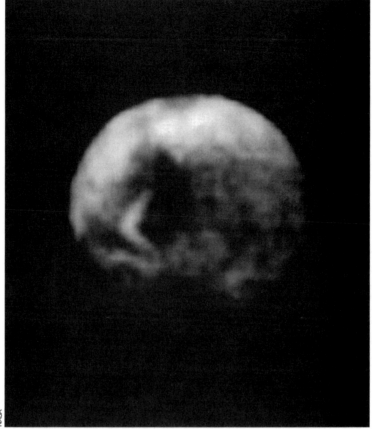

NASA

5-7 A distant view of Uranus' moon Miranda from Voyager 2. This is about the best picture we would have received from Voyager had not extensive in-flight improvements been made en route from Saturn. The resolution here is about 15 miles.

Neptune and Triton

In all the history of mankind, there will be only one generation that will be the first to explore the solar system, one generation for which, in childhood, the planets are distant and indistinct discs moving through the night sky, and for which, in old age, the planets are places, diverse new worlds in the course of exploration.

Carl Sagan

The discovery of Neptune in 1846 was the crowning glory of Newton's theory of universal gravitation propounded nearly 200 years earlier. In the first decades of the 1800s, several astronomers proposed that a planet in orbit beyond Uranus would explain perturbations of that planet. (That is, the actual positions of Uranus didn't tally with the calculated positions.)

C-1 M31, the Andromeda galaxy: our "twin" in the Local Group of galaxies. This photograph was taken through the 200-inch Mount Palomar telescope (compare with Fig. 1-5). This is about how our own Milky Way would look to beings living in M31. Note the two "satellite" galaxies, NGC 205 (upper left) and M32 (immediately to right of M31's nucleus), analogous to the Milky Way's Large and Small Magellanic Clouds. M31 is unimaginably far from us: light, which takes about eight minutes to travel from the sun to Earth, left it over two million years ago. To get some sense of the enormous distance, imagine all the individual stars in the picture to be raindrops on a window, very close, because they're in our own galaxy. M31 and its satellites are way out there, hundreds of times farther away than the farthest star in our galaxy. You can see its comparatively dense central nucleus surrounded by spiral arms of stars. Hundreds of billions of stars comprise M31 just as they do our own galaxy. If this were really the Milky Way, our sun would be about two-thirds of the distance from the nucleus to the outside, on the inside of one of the spiral arms. Hale Observatories

C-2 Total eclipse of the sun, July 11, 1991. In this rather underexposed photo, two sets of ruby-red solar prominences, or flares, are visible. The height of the one on the left is nearly ten Earth-diameters. Such flares can last for hours or even days. Barry Evans

C-3 Total eclipse of the sun, July 11, 1991. The film, being exposed for a longer time than for C-2, sees the delicate structure of the hot white corona. Our naked eyes, which have much greater ability to see contrast than photographic film, could easily see both the prominences and corona at the same time. This and C-2 were taken from Los Frailes, near Cabo San Lucas, Baja California within five miles of the eclipse centerline. Photographs taken on Kodachrome 64 through a TeleVue Renaissance 4″ refracting telescope, FL = 550 mm. Barry Evans

C-4 Proof that Earth really does tilt! As the Galileo spacecraft flew by Earth in early December 1990, it took this picture of Earth's south polar region. Notice Antarctica reflecting sunlight. In December the south pole is tilted towards the sun, so Antarcticans get 24 hours of daylight. NASA

C-5 A historic image: the first time the whole Earth had ever been photographed in color, November 10, 1967. A new color scan camera on the ATS-3 satellite had been carried aloft into geosynchronous orbit (so it remains in the same place relative to the Earth below) five days earlier. NASA

C-6 The Geosphere, showing a cloudless Earth, where summer reigns in the northern and southern hemispheres simultaneously. Land above 10,000 feet is assumed to be snow-covered. Images from hundreds of weather satellite photographs were turned into this true-color mosaic over a period of 10 months. Tom Vant Sant/The Geosphere Project

C-7 Is this how Mars looked about 3.8 billion years ago? The ocean fills present-day Valles Marineris. To the left, the volcanoes of the Tharsis Ridge are alive and well, with the middle one, Pavonis Mons, emitting a huge plume of steam and carbon dioxide. At the far left, Olympus Mons can be seen. The great flood channel running north is Kasei Vallis. Where it changes direction and runs east is the location of Figs. 4-12 and 4-13. Michael Carroll

C-8 Olympus Mons, largest volcano in the solar system. The base is about 360 miles across and it's three times higher than Mount Everest. In the absence of the mechanism of plate tectonics (which on Earth limits the size of volcanoes), Martian volcanoes can continue to grow so long as molten magma is available. Sufficient carbon dioxide and water vapor might once have poured from this and other volcanoes to create a climate similar to Earth's at the same time, over 3 billion years ago.
NASA and USGS, Flagstaff, AZ

C-9 A Viking lander on Mars. Artist's impression, made before Vikings 1 and 2 touched down in 1976.
NASA

C-1

C-2

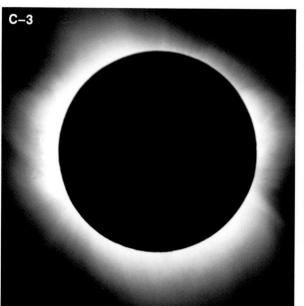

C-3

C-4

C-5

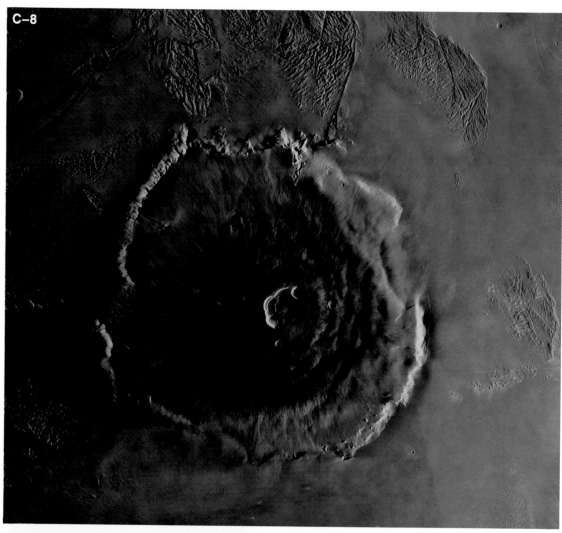

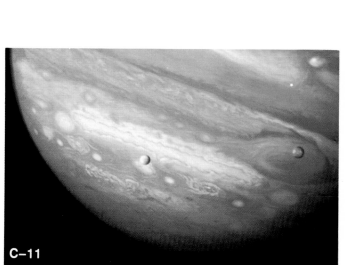

C–14

C–15

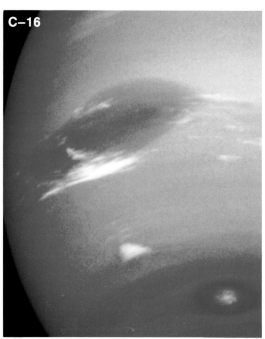

C–16

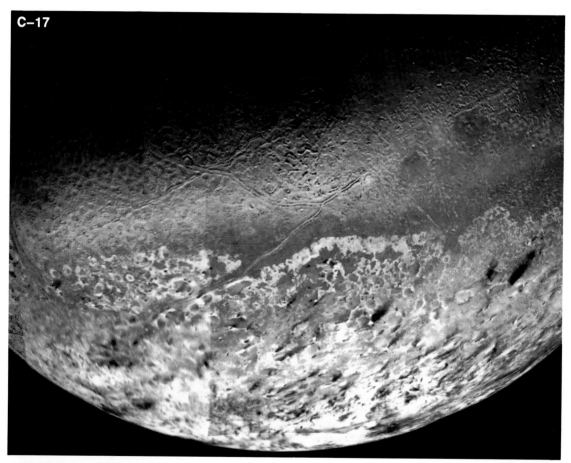

C-17

C-18

C-19

C-20

C-21

C-22

C-10 Mars from Viking 1. This color photograph was taken July 21, 1976, the day after the spacecraft's successful landing in Chryse Planitia, the Plain of Gold. The two Vikings were our surrogate eyes for several years from 1976 on, Viking 1 continuing to send back data and photographs for over 200 Earth days, until November 1982. Here, Viking looks towards the southeastern horizon at Martian noon. The reddish surface material is hydrated ferric oxide—rust—formed from the iron-rich soil in the presence of water and an oxidizing atmosphere. NASA

C-11 Jupiter, Io, and Europa. Io and Europa are two of the four major "Galilean" moons (so called after their discoverer) of Jupiter. Io, the orange sphere in front of Jupiter's "Great Red Spot," is the closest of the four to the planet, with Europa the next closest. Both are about the size of our moon, and like our moon, are locked in "synchronous rotation" so that the same side always faces the planet. The spot's red color probably comes from phosphene being converted into phosphorus. NASA

C-12 Io from Voyager 1, March 1979. Io is a little larger than Earth's moon. A plume from Pele, the first sulphur volcano to be discovered on Io, is visible on the upper "limb." NASA

C-13 A detailed mosaic of Pele made from Voyage 1 pictures. The geyser-like eruption reaches nearly 200 miles above the surface, while concentric yellow and brown rings show recent deposits from the volcano. The eruptions come from the two hills with a central valley "below" the visible eruption. Four months later, when Voyager 2 arrived at Jupiter, Pele was inactive. NASA USGS, Flagstaff, AZ

C-14 Saturn's rings from Voyage 1. The colors are computer-generated, representing different compositions size of material in the rings. Whereas only five rings were known before Pioneer 11's 1979 fly-by, Pioneer and the two Voyagers found thousands of individual rings. NASA

C-15 Astronaut's view as she touches down on Miranda some time in the future? Uranus is 65,000 miles away, nearly filling the background, with its faint ring system exaggerated for clarity. Notice Miranda's crazy surface: a deep canyon, impact craters and a patchwork quilt of colors. The mosaic was created from Voyager 2 images of Miranda and Uranus. The rings were artificially added. NASA

C-16 Neptune as seen from Voyager 2, August 1989. The upper atmosphere has an active meteorology, as exemplified by the "Great Dark Spot" (middle, left); the eye-like "Small Dark Spot" (bottom); and a bright spot of frozen methane cirrus called "scooter" (between the GDS and SDS). NASA

C-17 Truth is stranger than fiction. Triton's colorful and active south pole area, as seen by Voyager 2 in January 1989. NASA

C-18 August 20, 1977. Voyager 2 blasts off from the Kennedy Space Center, Florida atop a Titan-Centaur launch vehicle. NASA

C-19 A find! Antarctican meteorite hunter with a "regular" stony meteor. Her transport is in the background. Scott Sandford, NASA/Ames Research Center

C-20 An artist's impression of the catastrophic event believed to have occurred 65 million years ago in the sea near present-day Chicxulub, in Mexico's Yucatan peninsula. Travelling at perhaps 20 miles per second, the 6-mile diameter body is believed to have created a 3-mile-high tsunami and lofted massive amounts of dust high into the atmosphere, where it cut off sunlight to the surface. The front end of the body would have shock-heated the atmosphere to four or five times the surface temperature of the sun. Don Davis, Random House Inc.

C-21 Pterodactyls' view of the Chicxulub impact.

C-22 A tiny sliver of "shocked," or severely stressed, quartz from the Beloc layer, photographed in polarized light. Shocked quartz is only found in laboratories, at nuclear test sites, and in impact craters and ejecta. Dave Kring, Univ. of AZ

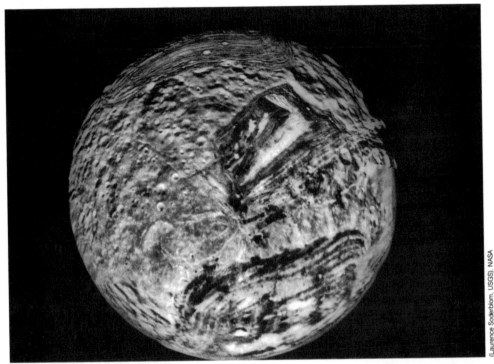

(Laurence Soderblom, USGS). NASA

5-8   A mosaic of high-resolution images from Voyager 2 resulted in this crisp computer-generated view of 300-mile diameter Miranda. (Compare with Fig. 5-7.) The south pole is in the center of the image. The extreme differences in topography were probably caused by the moon being shattered and subsequently accreting (possibly more than once), resulting in some of the original core material now being located on the surface. (Another possibility is that Miranda froze before the differentiation process was complete.) Miranda has been likened to ''a bizarre hybrid of valleys and layered deposits on Mars, combined with the grooved terrains of Ganymede, matched with (what some have called) compression faults on Mercury.''

Two men, one in England and the other in France, calculated the orbit of this "phantom planet" using Newton's formula. Unfortunately for John Couch Adams (the Englishman), no one was particularly interested in his prediction and it got shelved. Meanwhile in France, Urbain Le Verrier was also having difficulty getting heard, so he sent his calculations to the Berlin observatory in Germany. On the evening of the day the letter arrived, astronomer Johann Gottfried Galle easily found the planet, almost exactly where Le Verrier had predicted. Because Adam's prediction was virtually identical with Le Verrier's, both men are now generally credited with the discovery.

Our venerable surrogate, the Voyager 2 spacecraft, flew within 3,000 miles of Neptune and in a few hours, on the night of August 24, 1989, sent back more information about the planet and its moons than had been obtained from Earth since the planet had been discovered 143 years earlier. As we've seen, Neptune proved to be a much more interesting visual object than Uranus, despite being so far from

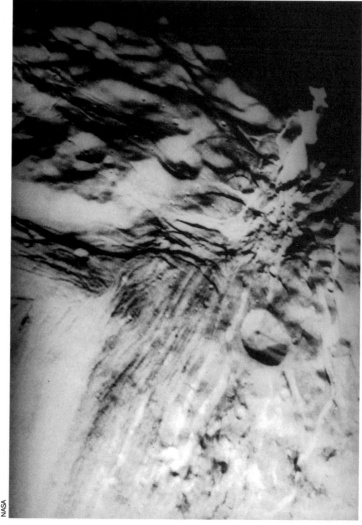

NASA

5-9 Close-up of part of Miranda from Voyager 2, showing cliffs rising nearly 10 miles above the valley floor. Miranda has feeble
gravity compared to Earth's (about one seventieth), so that a
rock thrown from the top of the cliff would take over five minutes to fall. (Compare this, for instance, with the highest vertical wall on Earth: Eigerwand, the north face of the Eiger in
Switzerland, just one mile high. A rock thrown from the top
would take 18 seconds to fall, not counting air resistance.)

the sun. (At 30 AU from the sun, Neptune receives one nine-hundredth of the sunlight available to Earth.) We believe an internal heat source is largely responsible
for Neptune's active meteorology. Another factor might also play a role: resistance
to tides raised by its nearby moon, Triton, which orbits the planet a little closer
than our moon orbits Earth.

Evidence for Neptune's warmth can be seen in the major meteorological features seen on Neptune by Voyager 2, including the Great and Small Dark Spots and a bright "scooter" (C-16). These vast storms and hurricanes tell us that Neptune has a very active atmosphere as it whirls around the planet at wind speeds of up to 700 miles an hour. Such features were totally absent in Uranus, which had been visited by Voyager three years earlier.

Voyager's last port of call in the solar system was Neptune's largest moon Triton, which managed to produce one final round of amazement for the Voyager scientists who by now, you might have thought, would have been inured to surprise. Triton is four-fifths the diameter of Earth's moon and is covered with ice caps of frozen nitrogen. Astonishingly for such a small body at such a great distance from the sun, it also has an active surface. To understand why, two factors need to be taken into consideration: like Jupiter's Io, Triton is close enough to its parent planet for tidal forces to create a significant energy source; and it has a 650-year seasonal cycle, resulting in very long summers for the poles. (This long cycle results from two phenomena: Neptune's long, 165-year orbit around the sun; and Triton's retrograde, or backward, orbit around the planet.)

Take a look at C-17, a mosaic showing Triton's bright south polar region. Does this remind you of anything . . . such as those experiments in the chemistry lab all those years ago? Remember heating some solid crystals in the bottom of a test tube and watch as they would first turn into vapor, then magically reappear as a solid ring higher up on the sides of the tube? It's called *sublimation*, the process of going from a solid to a gaseous state and back again while skipping the usual liquid state.

The gray band above the pinkish ice is equivalent to the side of your test tube where the vapor has sublimated. During the continuous three hundred or so years of summer at the south pole (where it's now midsummer), sufficient heat is absorbed for the frozen nitrogen at the surface to become a gas. As it drifts north, it becomes too cold to remain in gaseous form, and so condenses on the surface where we see it. This slow cycle has probably been repeating over and over for billions of years.

Other surface features, including frozen lakes and gigantic fissures (Figs. 5-10, 5-11 and 5-12) on Triton testify to its dynamic nature. At minus 400 degrees Fahrenheit, nitrogen is as hard as rock, but it is believed liquid nitrogen lies below the surface, and that under pressure, this liquid forces its way to the surface. That's the best explanation to date for at least one five-mile-high geyser-like plume of dark material captured in action by Voyager's cameras, and for at least 50 long streaks of dark material—presumably "volcanic ash"—downwind of other suspected volcano sites. What mechanism could create underground pools of liquid nitrogen? The likely suspect is a "solid state greenhouse effect." Solar radiation penetrates the outer solid nitrogen blanket (analogous to the gaseous carbon dioxide blanket in our atmosphere), but gets trapped by darker material a few feet below the surface.

Triton appears to be one of a kind, although, like so much about these distant frozen worlds, even that remark is debatable. Because it's the only major moon in the solar system with a retrograde (backwards) orbit, the suspicion is that it might once have been a free object, captured by Neptune at a comparatively late stage in

NASA

5-10 A frozen lake or "caldera" (basinlike depression) of an ancient ice volcano on Triton. It's about 120 miles across and is bordered by 600-feet high cliffs. The fact that we see such features and very few impact craters suggests that Triton has undergone melting and volcanism after the solar system's period of heavy meteor bombardment that scarred, for instance, Mercury and the highlands of our moon. Notice the relatively fresh impact crater left of the basin's center. The smallest features visible are about half-a-mile across.

the formation of the solar system. Mathematically, this is a tricky proposition—one that has been virtually discounted for the origin of Earth's moon. (See *Where did the moon come from?*). If it was a free object, this would put it in the class of bodies from which yet another oddity probably came, one we have yet to visit: the planet Pluto.

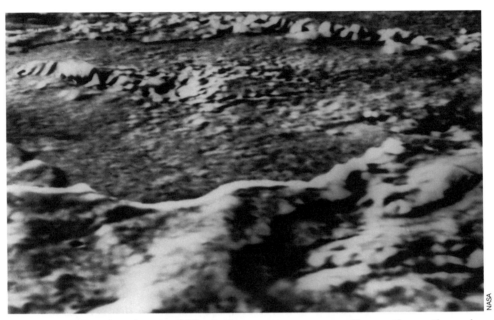

5-11 The caldera-like feature of Fig. 5-10, as an astronaut standing on the southern rim would see it, except that the vertical scale has been exaggerated 20 times. Supercomputer-processing using subtle information from shadows allowed this "view" to be made.

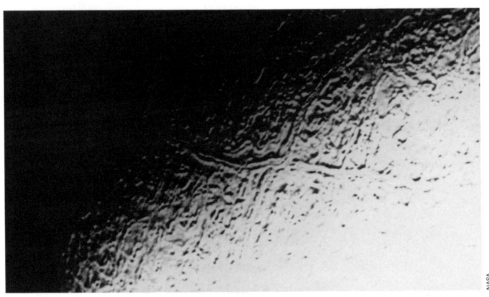

5-12 The surface of Triton. Not the intersection of two freeways, or even a close-up of a cantaloupe, but dropped-down fault blocks, indicating intense geological activity sometime in the past.

This idea, that Triton and Pluto are twins, has intrigued planetary scientists for decades. One day, when a mission to Pluto finally gets there, we should know for sure.

Trivia from Neptune

That star is not on the map!

Heinrich d'Arrest, who was assisting Johann Galle at the discovery of Neptune, 1846. (The "star" was Neptune.)

- Johann Encke had a double celebration on September 23, 1846: as director of the Berlin Observatory, he was on hand to confirm the finding of his subordinate, Johann Galle, for the first positive identification of Uranus; it was also his 55th birthday.

- Galileo almost certainly saw Neptune 234 years before Neptune's official discovery. He had been observing the motions of the four large ("Galilean") moons of Jupiter for about three years when he noted two stars very close to Jupiter. It's been calculated, from computer orbital calculations, that one of these was probably Neptune. In his diary entry for January 28, 1613, Galileo wrote that the two stars, ". . . were observed on the preceding night, but they [then] seemed further apart (. . . sed videbat remotiones inter se)." Because stars don't move relative to each other from night to night, it's a safe bet that one of his "stars" was Neptune. Unfortunately, he didn't follow up on the observation.

- Coincidently, two people (separated by a century) each discovered moons of Uranus and Neptune. William Lassell discovered Neptune's Triton in 1846, and Uranus' Ariel and Umbriel in 1851; Gerard Kuiper found Miranda (Uranus) in 1948 and Nereid (Neptune) a year later.

- The pictures we received from Voyager 2 at Neptune were sent via a 22-watt radio transmitter. That's one-fifth of the power of an average household light bulb. Travelling at the speed of light, radio signals took four hours six minutes to reach us from 3 billion miles away.

- No wonder we didn't know much about Neptune before Voyager 2 went there. Seen from Earth, it appears about as big as a dime seen from a mile away.

- Voyager 2 took advantage of a rare line-up of the outer planets to visit Neptune after flying by Jupiter, Saturn, and Uranus. Such a line-up last happened 180 years earlier, when Jefferson was president.

- Earth would fit snugly into a giant cloud feature of Neptune, the "Great Dark Spot."

- Although Pluto is usually credited as the planet farthest from the sun, the honor currently belongs to Neptune. In a highly eccentric orbit, Pluto is closer than Neptune to the sun from 1979 to 1999.

The flight of Voyager 2

When [Voyager 2] arrived at Uranus, it was twice as far away and twice as old [as when it passed Saturn]. Yet it had in fact become better: most of the spacecraft's subsystems had actually been improved en route.

Richard Laeser, William McLaughlin, Donna Wolf, *Scientific American,* **November 1986**

Much of what we know about Jupiter and Saturn, and virtually all our knowledge of Uranus and Neptune, comes from one little spacecraft that performed valiantly far beyond its original mission requirements: Voyager 2. This spacecraft is affectionately known as *The Little Spacecraft That Could*, which transmitted over 9,000 images from the far reaches of the solar system (Fig. 5-13).

5-13 Voyager spacecraft. The parabolic "dish" antenna points back towards Earth. Notice, below the body of the craft, the scanning platform, on which are mounted the visible light, infrared and ultraviolet cameras. Above, three gallon-jug sized radioisotope (plutonium) thermoelectric generators provide power. (The Voyagers are too far from the sun to be able to generate solar power.) The spherical tank containing hydrazine fuel for maneuvering is behind the antenna. The long mast off to the left supports instruments that measure the strength of magnetic fields. The body of the spacecraft is about the size and weight of a Honda Civic.

The astonishing thing about the spacecraft, which is about the size and weight of a Honda Civic, is that it was designed in the early 1970s and built for launch in August 1977 (C-18). Its electronics are ancient compared with modern technology. For instance, its on-board computers use 8K RAMs (Random Access Memories:

RAM chips in modern desktop computers have thousands of times that capacity), and its TV camera eyes use inefficient vidicons, compared with modern CCDs. Yet at the time of their manufacture, the Voyager spacecraft were two of the most complicated technological systems ever assembled, each with over 65,000 parts. Voyager 2 was officially designed to visit no planets other than Jupiter and Saturn.

Its sister spacecraft, Voyager 1, did just that. After passing through the rings of Saturn, it left the plane of the ecliptic. We can get a clue as to where Voyager 1 was then heading by the remarkable mosaic we've seen in Fig. 5-2.

In contrast, Voyager 2 stayed in the ecliptic. After flying by (and being accelerated by) Jupiter and Saturn, it went on to visit Uranus and Neptune. However, it was a considerably different spacecraft when it arrived at Uranus than when it had left Saturn five years earlier. The magic took place in those primitive computers. Engineers on Earth knew Voyager 2 would be hard pressed to take clear photographs of Uranus and its moons for at least two reasons: there's not much sunlight at Uranus (one four-hundredth of that reaching Earth), and Uranus and its moons spin sideways. Most planets spin approximately upright, at right angles to the plane in which they orbit. (Earth for instance is tilted about 23 degrees from upright, hence our seasons, while Jupiter is tilted 3 degrees). Uranus' axis, on the other hand, is more or less parallel to its orbital plane. This is why the challenge of photographing Uranus' moons was likened to "speeding on a bullet at night through the hole in the middle of a phonograph record while trying to get data on the outside grooves!" It was even worse than that—at 12 miles per second, Voyager was travelling ten times *faster* than a bullet when it flew by Uranus.

Obviously the technology used for Jupiter and Saturn and its moons wouldn't work very well for Uranus and even more distant Neptune. Long time exposures would result in blurry images, because the camera's scanning platform, on which the cameras were mounted, wasn't designed to "pan" while the image was being made. (Panning is a technique used to photograph a moving object, e.g., a racing car. The camera is swung around while the shutter is open, resulting in a crisp image of the speeding car with a blurry background.) The clarity of long exposures would also be compromised each time the spacecraft's tape recorder started and stopped, due to the torque of the motors. A way had to be found to allow the cameras to pan smoothly.

New and improved

The innovative answer was to erase the memory of one of the three on-board computers and to replace it with instructions for the following improvements:

- Instead of panning only the scanning platform, the whole spacecraft would rotate, thus keeping the target object exactly in the center of the field of view for exposures lasting up to 15 seconds. When finished, the spacecraft would rotate back to its previous orientation. This second step was essential, because its dish antenna had to point precisely back towards Earth for messages to be sent or received successfully.

- Whenever a tape recorder started or stopped, the spacecraft's guidance jets would precisely compensate for the slight twist that would otherwise occur.

- Images would be transmitted back to Earth in a compressed data mode, a very efficient method of sending photographs that had only been perfected after the Voyagers had been launched.

All of this meant that Voyager 2 was actually a better spacecraft when it arrived at Uranus in 1986 than when it left Saturn in 1981! For graphic proof of this, compare Figs. 5-7 and 5-8. Figure 5-7 shows Uranus' tiny moon Miranda as it would have appeared to us if Voyager's original imaging system had been used. Figure 5-8 is a mosaic assembled from the images we actually received from the new, improved system. In the first picture, surface features up to 15 miles across are resolved, while the mosaic resolves details down to 1/4 mile.

Similarly at Neptune, Voyager 2's improved panning system allowed us to obtain sharp images of the planet and its curious moon Triton, despite the fact that it's almost dark out there: they receive one nine-hundredth of the sunlight Earth receives. It took nearly everything we had to pick up Voyager's data from Neptune; 38 antennas on four continents were used to detect the faint signal, equivalent to one twenty-billionth of the power it takes to run a digital watch.

Sometime in the next twenty years, as the nuclear generators wind down, power on the Voyagers will drop below the threshold 245 watt level. Before then, however, the spacecraft might have lost their ability to point their antennas back towards Earth, as the diminishing amount of sunlight approaches the maximum sensitivity of the tracking sensors. The Voyager team is hoping that before any of that happens, one or both craft will reach the *heliopause*, the invisible boundary between the sun-influenced region of space and interstellar space. This would be surely be a fitting climax for the missions of two aging spacecraft that have forever changed our understanding of the outer solar system.

Pluto, the ninth planet

On the morning of 18 February [1930], I placed the 23 January and 29 January Gem [Gemini] plates on the Blink Comparator, starting on the eastern half. This was a most fortunate decision. Had it been otherwise, Pluto might not have been discovered in 1930.

Clyde W. Tombaugh, *Out of the Darkness*

Voyager 2 "flew" by Jupiter, Saturn, Uranus, and Neptune, four of the five outer planets of our solar system. A question I'm often asked is, "Why didn't it fly past Pluto as well?" When Voyager was launched in 1978, the four planets it visited happened to be in the right place at the right time. Each successive planet was ahead of the previous one in orbit round the sun, so mission planners could use the gravitational "well" of each planet to accelerate the spacecraft on to its next rendezvous. The process is called *gravitational assist*, or more commonly, the slingshot mechanism.

Even if Pluto had been conveniently placed (it wasn't, it was right on the opposite side of the sun), its orbit is so eccentric and elliptical that the planet is almost always unreachable by sling-shotting a spacecraft successively past Jupiter, Saturn, Uranus, and perhaps Neptune. The problem is Pluto's orbital path. All the other planets have roughly circular orbits, which are approximately in the same plane as Earth's orbit, the ecliptic. Not only is Pluto's orbit inclined at about 17 degrees to the ecliptic, but it's far from circular, causing the planet to spend nearly a tenth of its life closer to the sun than Neptune.

A moon of Neptune?

Because of its odd orbit, astronomers suspect that Pluto wasn't formed like the other planets. One theory says that it's one of a group of comet-like objects in orbit out beyond Neptune. Another is that is was once a moon of Neptune and was somehow thrown into its own orbit around the sun.

Finding Pluto in the first place was a triumph of good science and extreme patience. Percival Lowell, builder of the Flagstaff Observatory, started the search for a ninth planet in the 1900s, but it wasn't until 1930 that Clyde Tombaugh, working at Flagstaff with a blink microscope, discovered it by comparing pairs of photographs of the same regions taken at different times. Because stars stay in the same place from one photograph to the next, the motion of a planet is readily detected.

The astronomical symbol for Pluto, the superimposed letters P and L, could as easily stand for Lowell's initials as for the first two letters of the planet's name.

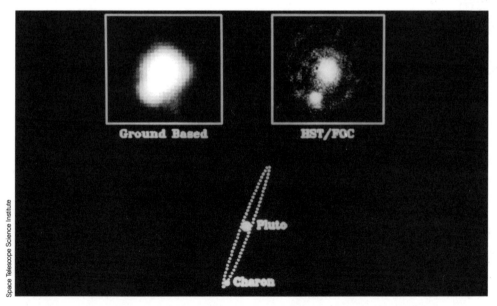

Space Telescope Science Institute

5-14 Pluto and Charon. Upper left, the best ground-based image taken to date, from the Canada-France-Hawaii telescope atop Mauna Kea, Hawaii. Top right, an image from the Hubble Space Telescope using the European Space Agency's Faint Object Camera. Despite Hubble's "myopia" (due to a fault in the geometry of the primary mirror), this image clearly resolves the separation between the two icy worlds. At the time of observation, Charon was near its maximum apparent angular separation of 0.9 arc seconds, see diagram below. This is equivalent to seeing a silver dollar (Pluto) eleven inches away from a dime (Charon) at a distance of forty miles.

Photograph by Andrew Fraknoi Astronomical Society of the Pacific

5-15 Clyde Tombaugh, who discovered Pluto in 1930, with James Christy, who discovered its moon, Charon, in 1978. Tombaugh is one of just three people ever to have found planets (assuming Mercury, Venus, Mars, Jupiter, and Saturn were "always" there!).

(You could also argue that the last two letters stand for the first two of Tombaugh's name!)

If Pluto was hard to find, imagine how much harder it would have been to detect a moon. However, in 1978 James Christy of the US Naval Observatory did just that (Figs. 5-14 and 5-15). Charon orbits Pluto once every 6½ days. This is all the information needed to calculate Pluto's mass: it's about one five-hundredth of Earth's. By measuring subtle changes in brightness when Charon crosses in front of its planet, astute investigators believe they have learned a little about the planet's surface and its tenuous atmosphere.

However, we won't get a detailed look until a spacecraft is steered to intercept Pluto, the smallest and most remote planet of our solar system. Pluto's distance from the sun varies from 30 to 50 AU (30 to 50 times the distance Earth is from the sun). One mission under consideration by NASA calls for a launch in November 2001 with an ETA at the planet in June 2015 via gravitational assists from Earth and Jupiter only.

The mission is overdue. Spacecraft have flown by every other planet, and our exploration of the solar system will remain incomplete until we receive photos from lonely Pluto and its moon Charon.

6
Comets, asteroids, and meteors

We suppose that the dry and warm exhalation is the outermost part of the terrestrial world . . . It . . . is carried round the earth by the motion of the circular revolution. In the course of this motion, it often ignites wherever it may happen to be of the right consistency, and this we maintain to be the cause of the shooting of scattered stars . . . a comet is formed when the upper motion introduces into a condensation of this kind a fiery principle not of such excessive strength as to burn up much of the material quickly, nor so weak as to be extinguished . . . The fact that comets when frequent foreshadow wind and drought must be taken as an indication of their fiery constitution.

Aristotle, *Meteorologia*, Revised Oxford Translation

In addition to the sun and nine planets with their 60-odd moons, the solar system includes thousands of comets and asteroids. Together these comprise a tiny portion of the entire mass of the system, yet they have had a disproportionately large effect on the life on Earth. Aristotle (above) notwithstanding, *comets* are small icy bodies with appreciable quantities of dust and other solid material in their composition. Most of them are believed to orbit the sun way beyond the farthest planets. *Asteroids*, also known as minor planets, are rocky (or, less commonly, metallic) bodies up to 600 miles in diameter that mostly orbit between Mars and Jupiter.

When a solid particle from either a comet or an asteroid collides with Earth's atmosphere, burning up as it does so, the result is a *meteor*, or *shooting star*. Occasionally, an extraterrestrial body reaches the ground without completely burning up, because it was so big (or possibly because it entered the atmosphere too slowly): it's called a *meteorite*. Very large meteorites create *impact craters*. Meteorites are generally believed to result from ancient collisions of asteroids, while most meteors originate in comets: they are "comet dust." Extra bright ones are called *bolides*.

So much for the definitions. Now let's take a closer look at these wandering bodies.

Comets are small (Halley's nucleus, for instance, is about 10 miles long by 4 miles across, the size of Manhattan Island) and their orbits are usually very eccentric. As Isaac Newton said after getting the hang of planetary motion, "Comets are a sort of planets revolved in very eccentric orbits about the Sun." Comet cores, or *nuclei*, have been likened to dirty snowballs, while their comas and tails—which only form in the vicinity of the sun—are tenuous clouds of gas and dust, sometimes millions of miles long. Most astronomers now believe comets formed at about the same time as the rest of the solar system (4½ billion years ago) far beyond the orbits of the planets, where they are now "stored" in a cosmic reservoir, the Oort cloud. This is a hypothetical halo consisting of comets that orbit the sun at up to one third the distance to the nearest star (between 30,000 to 100,000 AU from the sun). Any disturbance of the Oort cloud, such as a passing star, might initiate a rain of comets sunward, into trajectories where they might be visible to us on Earth. *Short-period comets*, like Halley's, come by at regular intervals, while others are seen only once. (Another theory for the origin of comets says they periodically accrete out of interstellar dust clouds through which the sun passes from time to time.)

Asteroids (also known as *minor planets*) are rocky bodies up to 600 miles in diameter orbiting around the sun. They're mostly found in the asteroid belt, located between Mars and Jupiter. Despite popular belief, they probably are not the remains of a tenth planet that ventured too close to Jupiter and broke up as a result of tidal forces—their total mass is far too small. More likely, they're debris resulting from several collisions of small bodies that had condensed between the orbits of Mars and Jupiter in the earliest days of the solar system. About 5,000 have been classified and named, the vast majority being less than 50 miles across.

Catch a falling star

Let's take another look at meteors and meteorites—we have plenty of data about these. For instance, you can go to many museums and actually touch a meteorite. No such luck with intact comets and asteroids in orbit.

Meteors, the ones that don't make it to the ground without burning up, consist mainly of particles ranging in size from a grain of sand to an orange seed. Regular meteor showers, such as the August *Perseids* and the December *Geminids*, result when Earth passes through a swarm of comet dust. When a comet gets close to the sun, some of its surface layer sublimates (i.e., the warmth turns it from solid to gas), releasing grains and lumps of material that become meteors if and when they burn up in Earth's atmosphere, at about 40 miles up. Every year Earth—travelling around the sun at 20 miles per second—intersects several of these "debris orbits," giving rise to annual meteor showers. For example, August's Perseids result from debris from periodic comet Swift-Tuttle.

Meteorites, on the other hand, are rocks large enough to survive the plunge through the atmosphere. That doesn't sound as strange today as it did 200 years ago. "I could more easily believe that two Yankee professors would lie than that stones would fall from heaven," said Thomas Jefferson in 1807. He was responding to well-documented accounts from Europe regarding a large number of "stones from heaven" that had fallen on the French village of Laigle, Normandy, four years earlier. Indeed, the root word, Greek *meteoron*, or "thing of the air" (hence *meteorology*), reminds us that Aristotle wasn't alone in believing meteors to be terrestrial phenomena, and that what we call meteorites were once no more than fanciful folk tales.

Thousands of meteorites have been found and classified. They are messengers from the past, remnants of the very early solar system, containing types of rock different from anything normally found on Earth. Some meteorites are enormous: an iron one that fell on South Africa in prehistoric times (the Hoba West meteorite) weighs about 60 tons.

Others leave great craters with little evidence of the impacting body itself. About 200 impact sites have been identified worldwide, including Meteor Crater, Arizona (Fig. 6-1) and Manicouagan Crater, Quebec (Fig. 6-2). While erosion and plate tectonics have virtually obliterated older terrestrial craters, most other bodies in the solar system are open history books of cratering (for example: our moon in Figs. 6-3, 6-4, 3-5, and Moon Maps 1 and 2; Mercury in Fig. 4-1; and Saturn's moon, Mimas, shown in Fig. 6-5. The highland areas of the moon appear more heavily cratered than the smoother "maria," which were flooded with molten lava after the worst of the meteor storms (See *Moon-gazing*).

We still have much to learn from comets and meteorites. Although comets are no longer considered portents of doom, and "stones from heaven" have graduated from folklore, the mysteries still abound. In this section, we'll consider an astronomical answer to the one question that might have enticed more students into the field of science than any other: What happened to the dinosaurs?

Meteor Crater, Northern Arizona, USA

6-1 Meteor Crater in Arizona, "The most interesting place on Earth," according to Swedish scientist Svante Arrhenius (1859 – 1927). Nearly 50,000 years ago, a relatively small meteorite, perhaps 100 feet in diameter, hit our planet at a velocity of about 45,000 mph. About 200 million tons of rock was displaced, leaving a crater nearly a mile across and 570 feet deep. Meteor (or "Barringer") Crater is the best preserved crater on Earth.

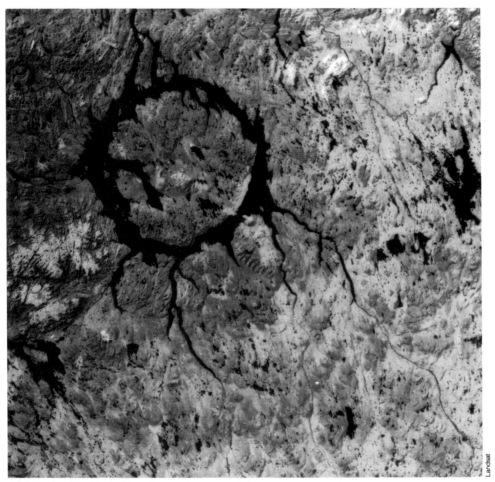

Landsat

6-2   One of the more obvious of about 200 known meteorite impact sites on Earth, Quebec's Manicouagan crater is about 40 miles wide, and was created about 200 million
years ago. In this Landsat photo, black represents water (which reflects light poorly).
The site was dammed some years ago, resulting in the view seen here: a lower ring
surrounding the higher central crater floor that bounced back after the impact. Compare this with Figs. 4-17, 6-4 and 6-5.

What's so special about a comet, anyway?

When beggars die, there are no comets seen:
The heavens themselves blaze forth the death of princes.

William Shakespeare, Julius Caesar

Comets are variously described as interplanetary vagabonds and stray members of
the solar system, but not too long ago (as Shakespeare indicates) a comet was a
portent of doom, a sign from up there to down here that something terrible was

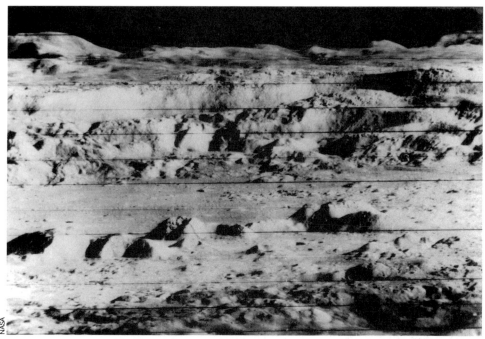

NASA

6-3 The moon's impact history is an open book, a near-perfect record going back at least three million years. This "picture of the century" (as it was called when first published) taken by Lunar Orbiter 2 in 1966, two years before the first manned mission to the moon, is a close-up of the crater Copernicus, one of the most prominent features of the moon (see Moon Map 2). Those mountains rising from the flat floor of the crater are 1,500 feet high, and it's about 150 miles from the horizon to the base of the photo.

NASA

6-4 Eratosthenes crater on the moon. This easily-observed lunar feature is a classic impact crater with a central peak. The latter results from the floor rebounding after impact. The crater is about 35 miles in diameter and two miles deep.

NASA

6-5 The Death Star? Actually, it's Saturn's little moon Mimas, just 240 miles across. It's been estimated that if whatever hit Mimas had been just a fraction larger (or faster), the moon would have shattered. Instead, we're left with a crater 80 miles in diameter with a four-mile high central peak. The crater is named Herschel after the family of pioneering astronomers: William, his sister Caroline, and his son John.

about to happen. The funny thing is, something always did! With plagues, floods, and other natural calamities, it was easy to find *something* bad to confirm a comet's warning. What made comets such credible harbingers was their sheer unpredictability—you never knew when one was coming.

Until 1682, that is, when 36-year old Edmund Halley saw a bright comet and subsequently showed its orbit to be very similar to those of comets seen in 1607 and 1531. Surmising that the three objects were in fact the same body travelling in a 76-year long orbit around the sun, he predicted it would return in 1758. It obediently did (16 years after his death), and the comet was named after him. More importantly, Halley showed that, instead of being sent by the gods, comets were part and parcel of our solar system, and at least some of them would return to perihelion (closest approach to the sun) on a regular natural, not divine, schedule.

The heart of a comet is its nucleus. The only comet nucleus we've seen (from faint images sent back from the European Space Agency's Giotto spacecraft) is that of Halley. It looks like a soot-black peanut the size of Manhattan Island, and appears to consist mainly of dirty water ice. What we see from Earth, with telescopes and sometimes with the naked eye, is the larger head (or coma) and tail (Fig. 6-6). Visible comets have long tails, thin plumes of dust swept away from the sun by solar radiation and by the *solar wind*—a stream of ionized particles constantly being emitted by the sun.

Photograph by Paul Mortfield

6-6   Comet Halley, as photographed on January 13, 1986 from Ottawa, Canada.

As we've seen, the best guess for the origin of comets is a hypothetical halo of gas, dust and proto-comets known as the Oort cloud, after the Dutch astronomer who proposed it. According to Jan Oort, this halo, a vast refrigerated reservoir of potential comets, is between 30,000 and 100,000 times farther away from the sun than is Earth. When something—perhaps a passing star—disturbs the halo, thousands of comets are sent sunward. Most of these are seen only once, but others, perhaps affected by Jupiter's gravitational field, become "short period" comets, regular visitors to our neighborhood.

The wrong-way comet

Wherefore if [Halley's comet] should return again about the year 1758, candid posterity will not refuse to acknowledge that this was first discovered by an Englishman.

Edmond Halley (1656-1742)

Earth and the other planets orbit the sun in an imaginary plane called the *ecliptic.* Imagine journeying far "above" the ecliptic plane, so that you can look down on our solar system. The most obvious object you'll see is our sun, which dominates the scene with its huge size and radiation. Around it orbit nine planets in roughly circular orbits. Earth is third out from the sun.

If you look carefully, you'll be able to see hundreds of tiny bodies also orbiting the sun, most of which are in highly elongated orbits. They're comets, and those whose return is regular and predictable, we call *short-period*.

Keep looking. Which direction do the planets go around the sun? Even though they orbit at different speeds, from your lonely vantage point, you'll see that they all move counterclockwise (or prograde). Now check out those comets. Are they also moving counterclockwise? You might inspect several and conclude that, indeed, they all are—but you would be wrong. Of the 120 known short-period comets, five orbit "the wrong way" (travelling clockwise around the sun), the most prominent of which is known to us as Halley's Comet. Some astronomers now believe they have an intriguing explanation for its odd-ball (literally) direction.

Charter members

Comets are generally considered to be charter members of the solar system, remnants of the original cloud of gas and dust from which the solar system formed. Surprisingly, we can test whether a body was once part of that cloud or whether it's a stray by comparing the ratio of a common element with other forms of that element, known as *isotopes*.

The nucleus is the heart of the atom. Elements exist for the most part with a fixed number of neutrons in each nucleus (the number of protons always remains the same—see *The Atom: Source of the Sun's Energy*). The 6-proton element carbon, for instance, usually contains 12 nucleons (6 protons + 6 neutrons) in its nucleus, so the common form of carbon is known as carbon-12, or ^{12}C. By varying the number of neutrons in its nucleus, an atom can assume other, closely-related forms. These rarer forms, having virtually the same chemical properties as the element's common form, are its *isotopes*. One isotope of carbon has 13 nucleons (6 protons + 7 neutrons) per nucleus, so it's called carbon-13, or ^{13}C.

When we examine carbon in our solar system, we find that the ratio of ^{12}C to ^{13}C is 89. Earth rocks, moon dust, the atmospheres of the giant planets, meteorites, in fact almost everything that has been measured, yields a ratio of approximately 89 parts of ^{12}C to 1 part of ^{13}C. Almost, that is, but not quite, everything. Telescopic measurements of Halley's Comet consistently show that the ratio of ^{12}C to ^{13}C is not about 89, as expected, but around 65!

So here we have a maverick object that not only is one of only five known bodies orbiting the sun clockwise, but which appears to have a significantly different common-to-rare carbon isotope ratio than almost everything else in the solar system. According to some investigators, this is a strong indication that at least part of Halley is unprocessed material. The solar system formed out of a cloud of interstellar gas and dust following a supernova—the dying explosion of a large star— nearly 5 billion years ago. Virtually all of it has been processed so that the original isotopic ratios have been modified, with the sole known exception of Halley, which appears to be virgin material from that supernova.

No wonder planetary scientists practically drool over the idea of obtaining a sample of the comet, because its "molecular memory" might be a unique record of the supernova from which you and I and everything around us originated. With luck, a future generation will obtain a sample of Halley when it returns in the year 2061, and those scientists dreams will become reality.

But wait . . . there's more

Having written a draft of the above discussion on Halley in 1990, I never considered that a postscript would be warranted, at least in my lifetime. Halley warms up slightly as it approaches the sun every 76 years, "growing" its coma and long tail as its surface melts a little. On departure, conventional wisdom says that Halley freezes solid, and nothing further happens until it's once again close to the sun.

So I was one of many Halleyites who was taken completely by surprise in mid-February, 1991, with the announcement that the comet appeared to have erupted. Two sharp-eyed astronomers at the European Southern Observatory in La Silla, Chile, were (according to the press release), "surprised because instead of the faint, tiny spot of light that was all the same telescope could see of Halley in 1990, there was now a rather bright and extended 'nebula' in the middle of the picture on the computer screen. In fact, this object was almost 300 times brighter than the image of Halley's nucleus was predicted to be." (See Fig. 6-7.)

What had happened? Maybe it had collided with another body: not impossible, but wildly improbable. Maybe some unknown source of internal heat reached the

Olivier Hainaut and Alain Smette, European Southern Observatory

6-7 Comet Halley's 1991 outburst. This image is a composite of eight individual photographs taken on February 12 of that year.

surface, like a volcanic eruption: again, not impossible, but given what we know about the structure of comets, pretty far-fetched. Perhaps the solar wind was interacting with the comet: a long shot again—at that distance from the sun, between Saturn and Uranus, the solar wind is very faint.

The truth is, no one really knows what happened and a month later Halley was almost back to normal. What a happy coincidence that the first comet to be recognized as such is proving far more intriguing and mysterious than Edmund Halley could ever have imagined.

Meteorites from Mars?

The young and chemically unique "SNC" meteorites . . . do not represent the bulk composition of [Mars], only that of the basalt lavas near the surface. Yet they do give us clues about deeper layers.

William K. Hartmann, *Sky and Telescope,* **May 1989**

Planetary scientists love samples. Twelve astronauts walked and drove on the moon between 1969 and 1972, the culmination of Project Apollo. Everywhere they went, they collected lunar soil and rock. In all, they brought back to Earth nearly half a ton of material, not to mention the small amount returned from a couple of Soviet unmanned sample-return missions. Since then, hundreds of scientists from all over the world have had a field day analyzing the samples to better understand the moon's origin and composition.

The moon is our closest companion in space, a mere quarter of a million miles away. After the moon comes Venus, and then Mars, which is sometimes within 30 million miles of Earth in its near-circular orbit around the sun. In 1976, four years after the last manned mission to the moon, two robot "Viking" landers touched down on Mars. They didn't send any samples home. Instead, they analyzed the soil at their landing sites under the guidance of on-board computers, and sent back a great deal of data about the composition of the Martian surface.

For planetary scientists, reviewing the data wasn't the same thing as examining chunks of Mars in their laboratories. If only they had some physical bits of Mars to examine, rather than radioed figures from the landers . . . but maybe they have!

One intriguing theory postulates that a few meteorites found on Earth originated on Mars. The evidence is sparse but compelling. Of all the thousands of meteorites that have been collected and analyzed, eight (to date) are quite different from the rest. They're known as the SNC group ("snicks"), after the places where they were originally found: Shergotty in India, Nakhla in Egypt, and Chassigny in France.

What differentiates them from all other meteorites is that they appear to have crystallized less than a billion years ago. That's 3 billion years *after* the asteroids—from where meteorites normally originated—had cooled. Also, all the SNC meteorites appear to have been formed in the presence of a strong gravitational field. Where do you find a such a field? Most likely, on the surface of a planet.

Identifying the source

The composition of the SNCs eliminated Earth and our moon as potential sources. Venus was also ruled out because its thick atmosphere precluded any credible mechanism for ejecting planetary material into orbit. Where else have volcanoes been active? The prime suspect was Mars.

The evidence became stronger when "shergottite" number EETA79001, from the Elephant Moraine area of Antarctica, was closely examined (Figs. 6-8 and 6-9). When cut open, it contained tiny inclusions of gas. Further analysis (in particular, of the proportions of the noble gases krypton, argon, xenon, and nitrogen) showed that the composition of the gas corresponded quite closely to that found in the Martian soil, based on analysis by the two Viking landers.

This correlation between the Martian surface and a handful of odd-man-out meteorites has been known for over a decade, but only in the last few years has anyone come up with a feasible mechanism by which fragments of Mars could make their way to Earth. It's obviously tricky: we don't generally see bits of our

6-8 Meteorite EETA79001, one of two "shergottites" found in Antarctica, and one of only eight "SNCs," meteorites thought to have originated on Mars. Notice the characteristic dark fusion crust, found on all fresh meteorites, formed by frictional heating as it entered Earth's atmosphere at a speed of perhaps 40,000 mph.

EETA79001

6-9 The saw-cut interior of EETA79001 showing black, glass inclusions and thin glassy veins in the light brown-gray host rock. The inclusions contain trapped Mars-like atmospheric gases and salt grains, the best physical evidence for a Martian origin of this and other shergottites.

planet suddenly leap into the sky and zip away towards other planets. The idea, proposed by a couple of researchers at Caltech, is that a large meteorite collided with Mars at exactly the right angle, billions of years ago. As it hit the surface, some of the Martian soil was vaporized and shot at high speed, like a jet, into space.

To show that this scenario is feasible, the investigators fired a high-velocity gun into rocks similar to those found on Mars. Using computer analysis, they showed that some of the particles could have escaped Mars' gravity, gone into orbit around the sun, and later been captured by Earth's gravitational field. Their long odysseys ended abruptly when they fell on India, Egypt, France—and Antarctica.

Future missions to Mars should tell us whether we've correctly identified these eight meteorites. It would be quite an irony if, while NASA was sending space vehicles to Mars, some few samples of that planet were already here, just waiting to be positively identified.

Meteorite hunting in Antarctica

. . . the world's coldest continent is also the world's best place to find meteorites.

Scott Sandford, astrophysicist and meteorite hunter

Finding a meteorite is finding a piece of the original solar system. By examining meteorites, scientists can learn a lot about the material from which Earth and the other planets originated. Every southern-hemisphere summer, searchers head to Antarctica to find more of them.

Why? Because, to paraphrase Willie "I rob banks because that's where the money is" Sutton, that's where the meteorites are.

Whereas meteorites that land on other continents are likely to be plowed under or eroded beyond recognition, Antarctica's ice and snow preserves them for hundreds of thousands of years. Better yet, they are concentrated into "ablation zones" by the natural movement of ice on the continent. NASA's Scott Sandford explains: ". . . large masses of meteorite-bearing ice run into mountain barriers. These barriers push the ice up into the constant wind, which wears away the ice. The meteorites are then left to accumulate on the surface for us to collect." (See C-19.) Every summer, the teams bring home up to a thousand meteorites, most of which are ordinary stony chondrites.

Out of the ordinary

Every so often, they come up with something out of the ordinary. Like, for instance, a meteorite from the moon. We've seen how meteorites could be blasted into space from the surface of Mars (See *Meteorites from Mars?*). A similar mechanism might bring chunks of the moon to Earth. Imagine a large body hitting the moon, throwing material high above the surface. To escape the moon's gravity well, material would have to travel at about 1.5 miles per second (5,400 mph), a not unreasonable velocity to expect from high speed impacts. (Compare this escape velocity with those of Mars and Earth, about 3 and 7 miles per second respectively. That is, a cannonball would have to leave the cannon at a minimum velocity of 3 miles per second to escape Mars' gravity.)

Once material is free of the moon's gravitational grip, it's quite possible for it to fall into Earth's stronger grip. A large enough chunk might fall as a meteorite, perhaps near the South Pole. This appears to be what happened in order for astrophysicist Sandford to find an odd-looking 1½ pound rock in the MacAlpine Hills of Antarctica, in January, 1989. He reports, "It did not look like the local terrestrial rock, and it did not look like a normal meteorite. Most meteorites have a distinctive dull black coating called a fusion crust, where the surface vaporized when it fell through Earth's atmosphere. This one was brownish-greenish-gray."

Sure enough the rock, officially cataloged as MAC 88105 (Fig. 6-10), was admitted to an elite club, one of only six previous lunar meteorites ever found (all in Antarctica) and at least ten times bigger than most of the others. It appears to have

NASA

6-10   The three-ounce stone that changed history for planetary sample scientists. ALHA81005,0 was the first lunar meteorite to be found on Earth. Discovered in 1982 by mountaineer John Schutt in Allan Hills, Antarctica, it's believed to have originated in the lunar highlands. The white inclusions come from calcium compounds. The scale cube (with the letter E) measures one centimeter (about four-tenths of an inch) on its side. This is one of about a dozen lunar meteorites that have been found on Earth, all in Antarctica. The largest, found by Scott Sandford, is about 20 times heavier than this one.

come from the lunar highlands, older areas about which we know little, because all but one of the manned moon landings were confined to the safer landing sites of the relatively level maria. (The exception, Apollo 16, landed in a low and geologically young highland region.)

Once again, we can only smile at the irony of finding bits of other celestial bodies in our backyards after putting so much energy into sending spacecraft to investigate those same bodies!

The dinosaur connection

The shock of one of these stars [i.e., a comet] which meets a planet without doubt would destroy it from top to bottom. It is true that would be a terrible hazard if one of these bodies which can move in all directions and dimensions in the sky came to meet a planet . . .

One can't doubt that most of the animals would perish if it happened that they were reduced to supporting the very excessive heat or to swim in fluids very different from their own or to breath strange vapors. It would be only the most robust animals and possibly the lowest which would remain alive. Entire species would be destroyed and one wouldn't find among those which would remain the order and harmony which had been there before.

Pierre de Maupertuis, *Essai de Cosmologie*, 1750, from *Les Oevres de M. Maupertuis*, Library du Roi, Paris, 1752 (thanks to Alan Hildebrand)

What's the connection between the Yucatan peninsula, a Nobel Prize winner and his son, and the extinction of half of all the life on Earth, including the dinosaurs? Very likely, a six-mile-diameter asteroid that most astronomers now believe collided with Earth near Merida, Mexico, 65 million years ago.

It's a tale worth telling. The first person to have wondered about a connection between comets and extinctions seems to have been a brilliant French astronomer and mathematician, Pierre de Maupertuis, quoted above. Evidence for the idea was hard to come by, however, and we have to move forward a couple of hundred years to pick up the story.

In the late 1970s, Geologist Walter Alvarez returned from a field trip to Italy with samples of rocks he'd found at the boundary between two periods of geological history, the Cretaceous and the Tertiary. This particular boundary is now enshrined in the lore of science as the K-T boundary (the K is for *Kreta*, Latin for chalk).

If you studied geology, you'll remember struggling with the names of periods such as Ordovician, Silurian, Devonian, and Jurassic. (You might have forgotten the order, but I bet you remember the struggle.) These periods do not divide the geological history capriciously, although I only discovered this fact some twenty years after learning about them in engineering school. Their boundaries mark major events, usually extinctions, in the history of life. The K-T boundary between the Cretaceous and Tertiary periods marks a particularly interesting event, from our point of view as mammals. Alvarez' samples from Italy tell the story: below (i.e., before) the boundary, many-sized fossils of one-celled marine animals called *foraminafera* abound; above (after), virtually all have disappeared, leaving just one small variety to press on into the future (Fig. 6-11). In all, it's been estimated that between 85 and 95% of all species of marine invertebrates, including ammonites, disappeared in a geological blink-of-an-eye at the K-T boundary, 65 million years ago. On land, everything weighing over fifty pounds disappeared abruptly, including the dinosaurs. Mammals, as you can confirm by looking in a mirror, survived and ultimately thrived.

Half-an-inch of clay

Geologist Alvarez was curious about a half-inch thick layer of clay between the rocks of the Cretaceous and those of the Tertiary. Could this clay be the key to what had actually caused such a sudden extinction of so many species? He wondered how long it had taken for the clay to be deposited. To estimate this, he needed to know the rate of sedimentation. How to estimate that? Not easy: it is, as he says, a major accomplishment to date a rock to an accuracy of a million years.

He discussed the problem with his father, physicist and Nobel laureate Luis Alvarez. Earth is bombarded with about 400 tons of micrometeorites every day, extraterrestrial particles smaller than grains of sand that drift down as cosmic dust from the upper atmosphere to the ground below. The physicist innocently suggested measuring the amount of one of several elements found in micrometeorites, but virtually absent from terrestrial rocks. He suggested *iridium*, the stuff that makes platinum jewelry harder but is otherwise virtually unknown. The necessary

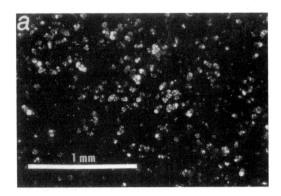

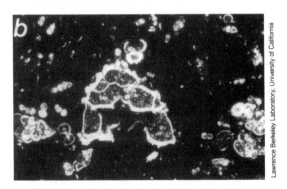

Photomicrographs from the Bottaccione Section at Gubbio of (a) the basal bed of the Tertiary, showing globigerina eugubina, and (b) the top bed of the Cretaceous, in which the largest foraminifer is globotruncana contusa.

Lawrence Berkeley Laboratory, University of California

6-11   Foraminifera from immediately above (a) and below (b) the K-T boundary. Younger sediments are, of course, above older ones. The magnified section from before the boundary shows an abundance of forams, both in diversity, size and sheer numbers. Something changed that dramatically, resulting in the paucity of the later sediments in the top photo. Both photos are at the same scale, about 30x.

measurements were made (with great patience and difficulty, using a technique known as *neutron activation*) and the surprises began. The boundary clay showed a concentration of iridium at least thirty times that of the rocks below (Cretaceous) and above (Tertiary)!

This investigation was a far cry from Luis Alvarez' regular work. He later wrote, in *The Adventures of a Physicist*, "I will probably be remembered longest for work done . . . in a field about which I knew absolutely nothing until I was sixty-six years old. The field is geology."

Within months of Walt and Luis Alvarez' 1980 paper announcing the discovery (co-authored with Frank Asaro and Helen Michel), other researchers reported anomalously high levels of iridium from the K-T boundary at sites scattered around the globe. Few iridium anomalies from other periods are known and to date the intensity of iridium concentration at the K-T boundary is unique.

What could be the cause of such an anomaly? A supernova, perhaps? That, however, would have also created plutonium in the clay, and none was found. Molecular clouds? No, Earth would have travelled too slowly through such a cloud to attain such an elevated iridium level. Through a process of elimination, the impact theory was born. Most researchers, representing many scientific disciplines, now believe the extra iridium came from a huge asteroid or comet that struck Earth, sending a vast cloud of dust into the upper atmosphere. It spread around the globe and later drifted slowly down to the ground, to be encased in the K-T boundary layer. The question was, could the impact have been so immense that it caused the mass extinction associated with the K-T boundary?

The five plagues

It certainly appears so. It's possible to calculate the size of the impacting body from the concentration of iridium and the average thickness of the clay layer in which it is found. It turns out that the meteorite was somewhere between 5 and 10 miles in diameter, which is quite enormous. A solid comet or asteroid 6 miles in diameter would hit Earth with the explosive power of a thousand times that of the total world arsenal of nuclear weapons. (Much of the energy comes from the estimated relative speed of the impacting body and Earth, which whizzes around the sun 20 miles every second—faster than any bullet.) The resulting magnitude 11 shock, measured on the Richter Scale, would easily have been felt around the globe. (See C-20 and C-21.)

It's estimated that such an explosion would have immediately killed everything within sight of the fireball, but that was only the beginning. Worldwide mass extinctions would have been triggered by such calamities as:

- Darkness. So much dust would have been injected into the atmosphere that sunlight would have been cut off from the surface of Earth for months. Photosynthesis would have virtually ceased.

- Cold. Not just sunlight, but sun-heat, too, would have been cut off. Studies of the resulting condition, termed *impact winter*, led researchers to consider a milder version of the "nuclear winter" phenomenon that would probably follow a nuclear war.

- Fire. Soot found in the K-T boundary layer indicates worldwide burning, triggered by incandescent material that was lofted into the upper atmosphere and spread around the globe.

- Acid rain. "Shock heating" of the atmosphere causes nitrogen and oxygen in the air to combine. The resulting nitrous oxide would have turned global precipitation into a nitric acid rain, wreaking havoc on marine animals and plants.

- Greenhouse warming. As if all this wasn't enough, flora and fauna which survived the cold would subsequently have had to survive a period of extreme heat. Water vapor and carbon dioxide are greenhouse gases (see *The greenhouse effect*). Both would have been released in large volumes into the atmosphere.

All this sounds a little like the plagues visited upon Egypt by a wrathful Jehovah in the Old Testament. In common with that story, there's bad news and there's good news. The bad news is, as we've seen, thousands of species were wiped out, including our back-of-the-cornflakes-packet heroes, the dinosaurs. The good news is that the resulting vacant ecological niches gave new opportunities to such groups as mammals.

The luck of the mammals

Mammals, which had been around for 150 million years when the K-T catastrophe occurred (nearly as long as dinosaurs), underwent an explosive phase of evolution after the event. Why did they survive when dinosaurs didn't? Perhaps because they were small, warm-blooded and born alive; or perhaps they were just plain lucky. Today, it's believed that luck plays a much greater role in evolutionary history than had hitherto been thought.

According to paleontologist Stephen Jay Gould, "Mammals may therefore have survived that great dying primarily because they were small, not because they embodied any intrinsic anatomical virtues relative to dinosaurs, now doomed by their size. And mammals were surely not small because they had sensed some future advantage; they had probably remained small for a reason that would be judged negatively in normal times—because dinosaurs dominated environments for large terrestrial vertebrates, and incumbents have advantages in nature as well as in politics." (*Wonderful Life*.)

Mammals. That's us, folks. We like to think we're the pride of the mammals, who themselves are the pride of the vertebrates, but look around. Every living creature and plant you see is descended from forebears that hung on through that cataclysmic time 65 million years ago. They won the lottery, and we, and the other tens of thousands of species with whom we share the planet, are the result. Let Gould have the last word: "In an entirely literal sense, we owe our existence . . . to our lucky stars."

Looking for ground zero

The clay bed is like a bookmark inserted between two chapters of the earth's history: one dominated by giant reptiles, the other ruled by mammals.

Alan R. Hildebrand, *Natural History*, June 1991

If you've been following the arguments in the previous essay, you might have anticipated the next question: If a gigantic asteroid or comet hit our planet 65 million years ago, where's the crater today?

A lot can happen in 65 million years. Back then, Greenland and Europe were still joined and the Indian subcontinent was adrift in the middle of the Indian Ocean. One fifth of Earth's surface has since been subducted: forced down and buried beneath land masses by the slow but inexorable movement of huge plates across our planet, the mechanism of plate tectonics (also known as continental drift). If the impact crater was devoured in this process, we'll never find it.

However, there's good reason to believe we *have* found the site of the impact, ground zero. At least, as I write (July 1991), there's an extraordinarily promising candidate in Mexico's Yucatan peninsula.

Getting warm

The impact would have been unimaginably violent. It's been estimated that 400 cubic miles of debris were carried aloft to the upper atmosphere (compared to Mount St. Helens' 1980 eruption when a paltry one third of a cubic mile of ash was ejected). Two distinct layers of material would have resulted.

First, the fireball layer. This fine, iridium-rich material would have spread around the globe and has indeed been found in about 100 sites worldwide from India to Canada.

Second, the ejecta layer, representing some 5,000 cubic miles—imagine that!—of shattered and melted rock would have been hurled from the impact site to a distance of at least 3,000 miles. The nearer you get to ''ground zero,'' the thicker you'd expect the layer to be. Since 1985, geologists have found many ejecta layer sites in North America, the western Atlantic Ocean, and the Caribbean. However, no ejecta layer sites have been found in Europe, Asia, Africa, or the western Pacific.

If the impact site was in the ocean, you'd expect to find evidence of a massive tidal wave, or an ''impact wave,'' as it has been called. ''An impact in the deep ocean would have created a set of waves three miles high,'' wrote geologist Alan Hildebrand in *Natural History* (June 1991). ''Reaching above the clouds, the waves would travel outward, like ripples on a pond, at several hundred miles an hour.'' Impact wave evidence again indicated an impact site in the western hemisphere. For instance, a chaotic outcropping in the Brazos River in Texas indicated that a massive tidal wave devastated the area (which was then hundreds of feet under water) about 65 million years ago. Other impact-wave evidence came from Arkansas, Mexico, the Caribbean (in particular western Cuba), and northern South America. The search area was beginning to narrow.

In February, 1990, Hildebrand visited southern Haiti, hot on the trail. ''One look at the K-T boundary in Haiti and the significance of the site becomes apparent. Directly beneath the thin gray clay of the fireball layer lies a pale greenish brown clay layer, one and a half to four feet thick (Fig. 6-12). Now resting high in the mountains, the clay—ejecta that settled on the floor of the ancient Caribbean Sea—contains some of the largest grains of shocked quartz [evidence of a massive explosion, C-22, together with *tektites*, Fig. 6-13] yet discovered and in quantities ten times that of other K-T sites . . . The most outstanding characteristic of the Haitian ejecta layer . . . is its thickness; at least twenty-five times that of any other ejecta layer, it indicates that the K-T layer is nearby.''

Moses comes to Yucatan

The first ''nearby'' candidate site was a possible 190-mile diameter crater 50 miles off of the north coast of South America in the Colombian Basin. Then an even more convincing site turned up on the north coast of the Yucatan Peninsula near the village of Puerto Chicxulub (CHEEK-shoe-lube), meaning ''horns of the devil'' in Maya. While searching for oil in the Gulf of Mexico, geophysicist Glen Penfield saw matching hemispherical patterns in the gravitational and magnetic surveys.

Alan R. Hildebrand, University of Arizona

6-12 The 18″ layer of greenish brown clay separating the Cretaceous from the Tertiary geological periods (the ''K-T boundary'') found in the mountains near the village of Beloc, Haiti. Its base is marked by the lower of the double bands around the handle of the foot-long geologist's hammer. In many other parts of the world, a ''fireball'' layer has been found at the boundary varying from one tenth of an inch to nearly an inch thick. The Beloc ejecta layer, which underlies the fireball layer, is at least 25 times the thickness of any other such known layer. The material here was hurled 500 miles from an impact site near Chicxulub, Yucatan, if researchers' latest ideas are correct. Not only does the ejecta layer contain the largest grains of shocked quartz ever found at the K-T boundary, it's also packed with tektites up to half-an-inch long.

Those patterns are now interpreted as an indication of gigantic impact crater, some 100 miles in diameter, buried over half a mile below the surface. Old drill logs and the few surviving drill cores (most were lost in a warehouse fire) appear to confirm that a major impact event occurred in the area at approximately K-T boundary time.

More confirmation for a massive impact crater came from an unexpected source. While searching Landsat satellite images for water sources used by ancient Mayan cities, researchers noticed that hundreds of water-filled sink holes were distributed in a semicircular pattern which matched Penfield's gravitational and magnetic patterns. This odd hydro-geological feature, called the Cenote Ring (cenote is the local Spanish term for sink hole, Fig. 6-14) provides surface evidence of the buried crater's precise location and size, because it appears to delineate an underground boundary between nonfractured limestone just inside the crater and severely fractured limestone outside the rim area (Figs. 6-15, 6-16 and 6-17).

Here, the circle seems to close, as geologist Walter Alvarez, co-proponent of the original impact theory, once again enters the picture. Searching in early 1991

Alan R. Hildebrand, University of Arizona

6-13 Tektites by the hundred from the Beloc layer. Tektites are tiny spherical and cigar-shaped pieces of material which originated from rock melted by the impact. The droplets congealed in mid-air into glass, most of which has subsequently been chemically altered. However, some tektites from Beloc still contain the original glass.

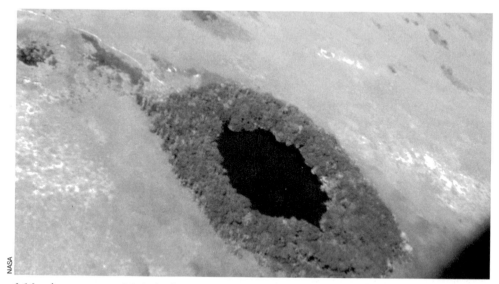

NASA

6-14 A cenote, or sink hole, in the northern Yucatan peninsula. Cenotes are small bodies of fresh water averaging 300 – 500 feet in diameter and varying in depth from 10 to 60 feet. Inland cenotes are deeper because the water table is a greater distance from the ground surface. Landsat images revealed hundreds of cenotes in an almost perfect semicircle in the northern Yucatan peninsula, denoting, it is believed, the rim of a huge buried impact crater 3,500 feet below ground.

6-15 One of the Landsat 5 satellite images taken from 400 miles up used to plot cenotes. Hundreds of cenotes, white dots in the photograph, define an near-perfect semicircle, the Cenote Ring. Water has a low reflectance and would normally appear black in the photograph, so the image has been reversed for clarity.

for evidence of a gigantic tidal wave at the K-T boundary, he and his co-workers identified a particularly unusual and complicated sequence of sediments. It lies near the coast of the Gulf of Mexico, 600 miles west of the putative Chicxulub impact site and close enough to have been caused by a giant meteorite landing there.

In a tongue-in-cheek allusion to another major marine event, they refer their first layer of twisted sediments as the *Moses bed*: a layer of scoured rock formed when the incoming tsunami (tidal wave) sucked up the sea, leaving a momentarily dry sea bed, which a moment before had lain quietly under 1,000 feet of water. The wave that followed, perhaps three miles high, created the *Pharaoh bed*. They think

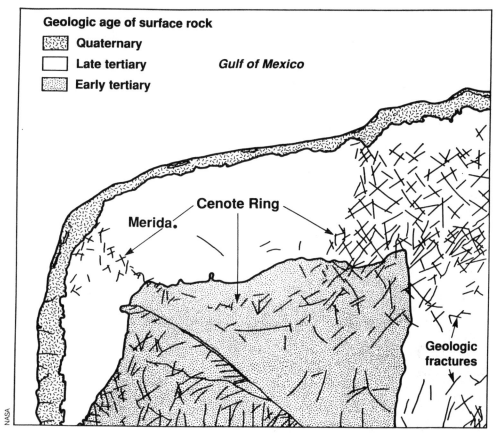

6-16 The Cenote Ring. Hundreds of cenotes delineate the buried impact crater. The fracture pattern in the porous limestone rock is thought to be caused by slumping of the buried crater rim.

they might have identified a third stratum of sediments laid above this as water sloshed to and fro in the Gulf of Mexico, a great standing wave seeking its own level. It's a giant version of what happens when you bathe with exuberance, so they called it the *Bathtub bed*.

Is this the end of the story? Hardly. Much of the above (in particular, the Moses and Pharaoh beds scenario) is open to debate. Future drilling at the site will tell us more, but other candidates for impact sites from the K-T boundary age can't be ruled out. Perhaps there was a comet storm, when several comets hit Earth within a (geologically) short period or time, or perhaps, as has been suggested, one large comet broke up and three pieces hit us more or less simultaneously.

Whatever the final outcome, the tale of how an unusually high level of the rare element iridium from an outcropping in Italy led to the site of an impact that might have caused the death of the dinosaurs will forever stand as a rare and imaginative piece of scientific detective work. Pierre de Maupertuis would have been proud.

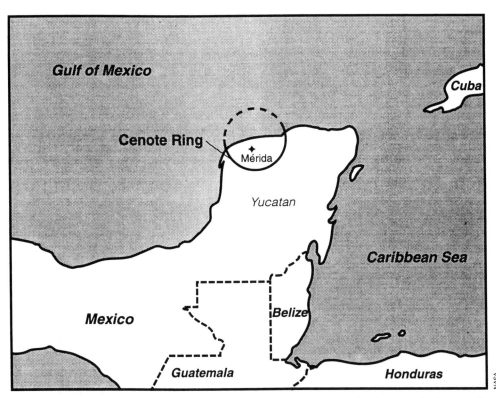

NASA

6-17   Location of the Cenote Ring. Chicxulub, for which the putative impact site is named, is 30 miles northeast of Merida. The broken line approximates the limits of gravitational and magnetic anomalies found during oil exploration surveys.

Miscellany: Comets, asteroids, and meteors

Meteorites are tantalizing gifts of new information about the solar system, just waiting to be unwrapped.

Harry McSween, Jr., *Meteorites and Their Parent Planets*

- Most meteors are seen after midnight, because then we're looking in the general direction of where we going in our orbit around the sun. Instead of meteorites "trying to overtake us," as is the case earlier in the night, we start meeting them head-on, so we see more of them.

- Early astronomers, self-styled "celestial police," started searching for a planet between Mars and Jupiter in 1800. They were convinced a planet had somehow been missed, due to an arithmetical coincidence known as Bode's Law. In 1772, German astronomer J.E. Bode showed that the distance of the known planets from the sun followed a regular pattern. (Titus of Wittemberg had first noticed it.) There was a gap, however, between Mars and Jupiter, and the "police" were determined to fill it.

- Instead they found asteroids. The first to be discovered, Ceres, was found on New Year's day, 1801. At 600 miles in diameter, it's also the largest, containing about half the total mass of all the asteroids. (However, the discoverer, M. Piazzi, wasn't a member of the "police.")

- Vesta is the only asteroid, or minor planet, visible to the naked eye, and then only at opposition and under exceptional viewing conditions. Discovered in 1807, it was the fourth such body to be found.

- Shortly before Luis Alvarez died in 1990, a newly-discovered asteroid was named after him and his son Walter. Discovered in 1985, Asteroid Alvarez seems a fitting tribute to the physicist and geologist who proposed the collision hypothesis for dinosaur extinction (even if some scientists now believe a comet, not an asteroid, caused it).

- Not all asteroids orbit the sun between Mars and Jupiter. For instance, the Apollo objects are irregular lumps of rock that cross the orbit of Earth. A few dozen are known, none more than a few miles in diameter.

- Some asteroids travel in groups. One pair of groups, collectively known as the *Trojans*, move in the same orbit as Jupiter at two gravitationally stable points, 60 degrees ahead of and 60 degrees behind Jupiter. They number at least a thousand in all.

- Asteroid number 2060, Chiron, is unique in that it spends five-sixths of its 51-year orbit beyond Saturn. It was discovered by the Palomar Observatory in 1977.

- Showers of comets might "fall" in towards the sun from the Oort cloud on a regular basis. Depending on how you interpret the data, analysis of past mass extinctions might indicate that they occur regularly, every 26 million years or so. (Don't worry, the next one isn't due for 15 million years.) The front-running explanation for such a cycle of comet storms is *Nemesis*, a hypothetical small, dim star in a 26 million year orbit about the sun that regularly disrupts the Oort Cloud. Astronomers are looking for it.

- Opinions vary on whether anyone has actually been killed by a falling meteorite. Applying the "extraordinary claims require extraordinary evidence" criterion it seems unlikely. The earliest *Meteorite Kills Man* story (as reported in *Sky and Telescope*, March, 1991) dates to over three thousand years ago. The Hittite army of Mursilis II (1339 – 06 B.C.) "saw a brilliant object, possibly a meteorite, which passed over their heads [and hit the enemy's king who] was first stricken in his knees and afterwards died of the effects." *Sic gloria transit*

Appendix
Viewing the nearby heavens

All other creatures look down toward the earth, but man was given a face so he might turn his eyes towards the stars and his gaze upon the sky.

Ovid

Binoculars for the night sky

The popular image of the amateur astronomer usually includes an unwieldy telescope that barely fits in the back of a station wagon. This picture belies the fact that most amateurs started their stargazing careers with nothing more sophisticated than a good pair of binoculars. Indeed, there's a lot to be said for using binoculars instead of telescopes for certain types of viewing.

The great advantage of a pair of binoculars is that they can sweep out vast sections of the night sky with no more effort than a little arm movement. Hardy comet and nova (*new* star) seekers use sophisticated binoculars for that very reason: in minutes, they can check out great swaths of sky for any changes, something virtually impossible to do with a telescope.

The most popular binoculars are the 7×35 size, meaning that they magnify seven times and have the same light gathering ability as a pair of 35 millimeter (1.4 inch) diameter telescopes. That doesn't sound like much until you remember that Galileo discovered the four main moons of Jupiter with a telescope having about the same specifications. For meandering through the Milky Way, for seeing craters on the moon, and even, when held steadily, for spotting Jupiter's moons, 7×35 binoculars are fine.

Better for astronomical purposes is the 10×50 size, which magnify 10 times and have twice the light gathering power of 7×35's. With these, you can enjoy truly awesome views of star clusters like the Pleiades and Hyades, and find (but not examine in detail) many galaxies and nebulae. They appear as faint wisps of light, which might inspire you to seek out the view from a larger telescope, or at least to check out photographs of these deep sky objects in books and magazines (see, for instance, C-1).

The trick with binoculars is to hold them steadily. Unlike astronomical telescopes, which are designed to be mounted on sturdy tripods, normal binoculars are usually dependent on our human frames for stability. There are many ways to assist this stability: try lying on your back for overhead objects, or hold your binoculars against a fence post or car top to prevent natural body shake. When you have the object you want to observe in your field of view, relax, take a deep breath, and gaze while not breathing, arms firmly to your waist, to minimize movement.

Better yet is a stable mount. If you own a photographic tripod, all it takes is a rubber band to create a perfectly useful mounting for your binoculars. Otherwise, a long stick stuck in the ground at a suitable angle, with a short cross piece nailed to the top, will do the same job reasonably well. You'll find a mount particularly useful if you use the Moon Maps in this section to begin to familiarize yourself with the lunar surface.

It's important not to rush things. First get comfortably and warmly seated. Your eyes take 20 minutes or so to get into their night-vision mode. Whether you're looking through binoculars or a telescope, the "seeing" will come and go, in response to thermal movements of atmospheric cells overhead. Every so often, you'll be rewarded with a split-second of clarity. That's why a drawing of a solar system object by an experienced viewer (especially when a high-power telescope was used) is so detailed compared to a photograph of the same object: they've captured the planet at the perfect moment. May you have many such moments.

Three-dimensional space

Another advantage of binoculars is the sense of vastness they engender, a sense that's usually missing when viewing through a telescope. Because I'm so used to interpreting the world around me with both eyes, a monocular telescopic view often feels artificial and stilted. So when both my eyes send information simultaneously to my brain (as with binoculars), I often experience an awesome, dizzying feeling as I drink in those huge draughts of three-dimensional space. Binoculars help transcend my Earthbound feeling of looking *up* at the stars, and instead they give me the weird sensation of being *out* there, with no up or down for reference. Other than being an astronaut, I don't think there's anything quite like it to experience the vastness of space.

Planets through binoculars

The truth is, binoculars are not the greatest way to view planets: to really enjoy them, a telescope is essential. What binoculars will do is allow you to note the difference between a star and a planet, because you'll at least be able to resolve several planetary disks (as opposed to pinpoints of stars), and to inspire you to check out the telescopes at your local astronomy club (which is probably listed in the annual astronomy resource guide in September's *Sky and Telescope*). Having said that, however, there are a couple of planets worth looking at through binoculars: Venus and Jupiter. Venus is a curiosity because over the weeks and months, it exhibits phases as it changes size (see Fig. 4-4). Otherwise it's featureless. Jupiter is exciting because a steadily-supported pair of binoculars will show the four Galilean moons. They are small, pinpoints only, but quite distinctive for one reason: they're in line. You'll almost always see either three or four (one might be in front of or behind the planet), and you'll know that you have correctly identified them because you'll be able to connect them with an imaginary line that passes right through Jupiter. Sometimes you'll see all four on the same side of the planet, although it's more likely you'll see some on one side and some on the other. The important thing is to sketch their location (as Galileo did, when he discovered them), then do the same thing the next night, and the next, and so on. After following their movements for a week or two, it will be obvious which moon is which and how long they each take to revolve around Jupiter. Here's what you're seeing:

Position	Name	Diameter	Orbital period
1 (innermost)	Io	2,300 miles	42 hours
2	Europa	2,000 miles	3½ days
3	Ganymede	3,300 miles	7 days
4	Callisto	3,000 miles	17 days

Of the other visible planets, Mercury and Uranus are just specks (Uranus' methane causes it to appear a blue-green color). Other than its obvious orange color, Mars' features are too faint and fuzzy to be seen through binoculars. Also, Saturn's rings are too small to be seen, although you might notice that its yellow disk appears elongated when the rings are tilted towards us (see *The rings of Saturn*).

The moon through binoculars

Our moon is often an underrated quarry for binocular viewing, spurned perhaps because it's so readily available. Yet the process of familiarizing oneself with the moon's face is a rewarding one, for then it becomes an old friend, available almost any night for a minute or an hour of company.

The photographs and key maps that follow are orientated to the way we normally see the moon, so they are correct for binoculars (most telescopes invert the image). Two images are presented: Moon Map 1 is a composite image of the first and third quarter moons, so half the moon is illuminated from the right and the other half from the left; Moon Map 2 shows the full moon. Both images are included because, as you'll see at a glance, certain features (the most obvious is the crater Tycho) are prominent in one, and virtually absent in the other. By using both images at the appropriate time of the lunar month, you should be able to identify all of the major features. (If you don't see a feature in one map, try the other.)

Follow the moon through a complete 29½ day lunar cycle, from full to new and back to full again. Each night will bring new treasures, as the sun's shadow slowly moves across the moon's face, highlighting one feature after another. The terminator—the line dividing the sunlit from the dark regions—is always full of interest. Craters are etched three-dimensionally, long shadows fall across the maria, and isolated peaks shine through from the darkness beyond the shadow line. The two Moon Maps show only the major features. Even with binoculars, you'll be intoxicated with the crisp details. After which, you will find it hard to stay away from telescopes (I hope).

Lick Observatory

Moon Map 1 Composite of first and third quarter moons. The key map identifies the most prominent features visible through binoculars.

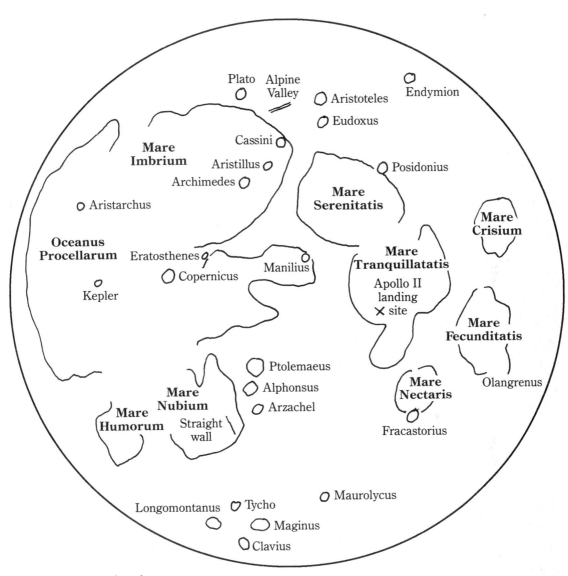

Moon Map 1   continued

Moon Map 2 Full moon. Notice how fewer craters are visible than in sideways-lit Moon Map 1.

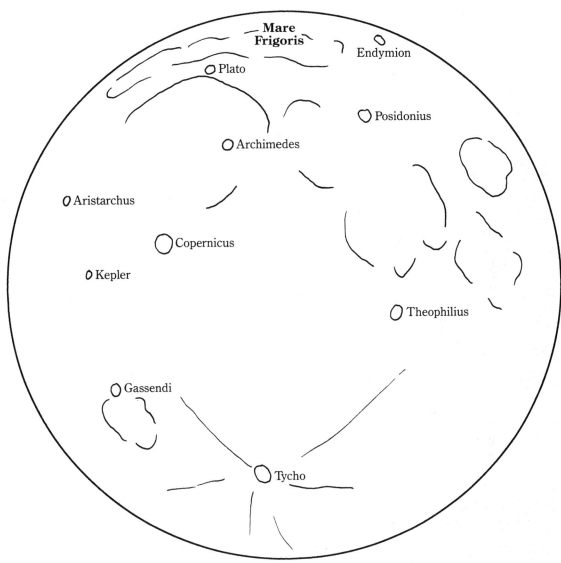

Moon Map 2   continued

Glossary

accretion "Snowball" mechanism whereby small particles are attracted to each other by gravity, coalescing into larger particles; these particles accrete into yet larger particles, and on and on in a hierarchy of sizes. The moons and planets of the solar system are thought to have formed by accretion from swarms of dust grains. Also known as *aggregation*.

albedo Measure of reflected light. A perfect mirror has an albedo of 1.0, while an ideal black surface that absorbs all incident light has an albedo of zero. The moon has an albedo of 0.07, meaning it reflects 7% of the light it receives from the sun.

Andromeda galaxy Our "twin" galaxy, a spiral galaxy approximately the size and shape of our own Milky Way galaxy. It's a little over two million light years away and can be seen by the unaided eye as a fuzzy oval patch of light under dark skies in the constellation Andromeda. (See C-1.)

angular momentum Measure of the energy of a rotating object or system, depending on the overall mass and its distribution, and the rate of rotation. The fact that angular momentum is a conserved quantity can be observed, for example, in a spinning ice skater: when she pulls in her arms, her rate of spin increases.

aphelion Point at which an object in solar orbit is farthest from the sun.

Apollo group Asteroids having perihelia within Earth's orbit.

Apollo mission U.S. program to put a man on the moon, originally proposed by John Kennedy in 1961. The method used was to launch a "command and service module" and a "lunar module" atop a Saturn V launch vehicle. The first manned lunar landing took place on July 20, 1969, with Apollo 11 crew members Neil Armstrong and Buzz Aldrin. Mike Collins remained in lunar orbit in the command module. In all, six Apollo missions put 12 men on the moon. The program was prematurely terminated in 1972 with Apollo 17.

asteroid   One of thousands of small (compared to planets) rocky objects in orbit around the sun. Also known as *minor planet.*

astronomical unit (AU)   Average distance between the sun and Earth, about 93 million miles (or 500 light seconds.)

atom   Traditionally, the smallest possible particle that can't be subdivided. The atom is now regularly "split." Most of the mass of an atom is concentrated in the central nucleus, comprised of protons and neutrons. Negatively-charged electrons are perhaps infinitesimally-small particles "in orbit" around the nucleus. (The quotations around "in orbit" refer to the quantum vagueness of their statistically-defined positions.)

atomic number   Number of protons in the nucleus of an atom.

Big Bang   Originally a term of derision by "steady-state" theorist Fred Hoyle (who didn't and still doesn't believe in it), the Big Bang cosmological model states that all matter and energy originated in an explosion (the *primordial fireball*) some 15 billion years ago. The model has been generally accepted by cosmologists who point to the many lines of evidence (e.g., the "background radiation" and the relative abundances of elements in the universe) that support it; however, a significant minority of scientists, in particular astrophysicist Halton Arp, contest the basic assumptions of the model.

bolide   Particularly bright meteor that explodes as it enters Earth's atmosphere.

brown dwarf   "Wannabe" star having a mass between 10 and 80 times that of the sun, in which short-lived nuclear fusion occurs. None have been found to date.

caldera   Basinlike depression resulting from the explosion or collapse of the center of a volcano.

Cassini/Huygens mission   Combined NASA-ESA mission to Saturn, scheduled for launch in April, 1996, assuming funds are available. When it reaches Saturn late in 2002, in addition to a detailed look at the Saturnian system, a probe (Huygens) will be dropped into the atmosphere of Titan (the solar system's only moon possessing an appreciable atmosphere).

comet   Minor member of the solar system, a small body generally thought to resemble a large dirty snowball. Most comets are thought to reside in the Oort Cloud at great distances from the sun. Short period comets are those that are in an elliptical orbit about the sun with a period of less than 150 years, e.g., Halley's Comet, which has a period of about 76 years.

corona   Bright, hot (over a million K), outermost part of the sun's (or any star's) atmosphere. Dramatically visible during a total eclipse of the sun. (See C-3.)

Comet Rendezvous/Asteroid Flyby Mission (CRAF)   Planned mission to flyby asteroid Hamburga (truly!) and comet Kopff. Earliest launch date is August 1995, assuming funds are forthcoming.

differentiation   Process in which denser materials migrated to the cores of planets and larger moons early in their history. For instance, in the case of early molten Earth, originally homogeneous rock separated into denser and lighter materials, resulting in Earth's interior being iron, while less dense silicate compounds are now closer to the surface.

eclipse   Blocking of sun's light by another body. Best known are solar and lunar eclipses. During a solar eclipse, the (new) moon passes between the sun and

Earth. If the moon is close enough and directly in line, the sun's disk is completely cut off from Earth's surface and a total eclipse results. If it's not in line, we see a partial eclipse. If it's in line, but too far from Earth, we experience an annular (ring) eclipse. A lunar eclipse (full or partial) results from Earth's shadow being cast on the (full) moon.

ecliptic Imaginary plane in space defined by Earth's orbit around the sun. Other than Pluto, the orbits of all planets lie roughly in the ecliptic, so we always see them (and the sun and moon) in a band within a few degrees of the ecliptic.

electron Elementary atomic particle possessing negative charge, little or possibly no size, and a mass about one two-thousandth that of the other "basic" elementary particles, the proton and the neutron.

elongation Angular distance between the sun and a planet, as measured from Earth.

equinox Moment when the sun is directly over Earth's equator, favoring North and South Poles equally. We experience two every year: the spring (vernal) equinox is on or close to March 21; the fall (autumnal) equinox is on or close to September 21. (See Fig. 3-8.)

escape velocity Minimum velocity needed for a body to escape from another body. Escape velocity from Earth's surface is about 7 miles per second; moon, 1.5 miles per second; sun, 400 miles per second.

European Space Agency (ESA) Consortium of 14 European countries for civilian space projects. The countries are: Austria, Belgium, Denmark, West Germany, Finland, France, Ireland, Italy, Netherlands, Norway, Spain, Sweden, Switzerland, and the United Kingdom.

fission Splitting. One old theory explained the moon's origin by fission of the original Earth-moon body. In nuclear physics, fission of nuclei such as those of uranium or plutonium into lighter nuclei results in mass being converted into energy: the atomic bomb.

fusion Coalescing. Hydrogen bombs fuse nuclei of hydrogen (or its isotopes) into heavier nuclei. This "thermonuclear" process powers the sun. (See Fig. 2-4.)

galaxy Conglomeration of stars (and gas and dust) held together by mutual gravitational attraction. Our galaxy is known as the Milky Way.

Galilean moons The four largest moons of Jupiter (Io, Europa, Ganymede, and Callisto, in increasing distance from the planet), discovered in 1610 by Galileo.

Galileo mission Mission to Jupiter (launched in October 1989). On arrival in 1996, a probe will be released for descent into Jupiter's atmosphere. The spacecraft's complicated trajectory includes gravitational assists from Venus (once) and Earth (twice). Success of the mission depends on the primary antenna being opened.

gravitational assist (or "slingshot" mechanism) Technique used by space mission planners to increase the velocity of spacecraft by sending them close enough to planets to acquire some of the planet's own momentum in its orbit around the sun.

gravity One of the four known forces in the universe, and the only one to have an appreciable effect over large distances. In Newtonian terms, any body is attracted to any other body by an invisible force proportional to the product of the masses of the two bodies divided by the square of their distance apart. (See Fig. 1-8.)

greenhouse effect   Mechanism whereby atmosphere of a planet (or moon) can trap heat energy from the sun. An atmosphere containing, e.g., carbon dioxide and water vapor, is transparent to visible light from the sun, but partially opaque to resulting infrared radiation from the planet's surface. (See Fig. 4-2.)

helium   Second lightest and second most abundant element. Its most common form (helium-4) consists of two protons and two neutrons in the nucleus orbited by two electrons.

highlands   Term applied to mountainous terrain on the moon untouched by molten lava that flowed into the lower areas ("maria") over 3 billion years ago. The highlands appear lighter gray than the maria.

Hubble Space Telescope (HST)   First large telescope in space, in Earth orbit. Launched in 1990, inaccurate geometry of its primary mirror has compromised its performance, particularly for very faint objects. A "prescription lens" is scheduled to be installed in 1994.

hydrogen   Light colorless gas that, given enough time, turns into people (!); the lightest and most common element. In its most abundant form, a proton orbited by an electron.

impact crater   (Usually) round crater formed by the impact of a small body on a larger one. The best preserved impact crater on Earth is Arizona's Meteor Crater (Fig. 6-1). All large solid bodies in the solar system have impact craters. On bodies lacking volcanism or plate tectonics, a clear record of impacts dating to the early days of the solar system is seen.

isotopes   Forms of an element with different numbers of neutrons in the nuclei. The number of protons is unchanged, and the chemical properties of different isotopes are virtually identical.

JPL   Jet Propulsion Laboratory, Goldstone, California. A space research and engineering institution run by the California Institute of Technology under a contract from NASA.

K-T boundary   Geological boundary between the Cretaceous and Tertiary periods, roughly 65 million years ago. A time of mass extinction, notably of the dinosaurs and other large land animals, although most species of marine animals also died. Believed by many scientists to have been precipitated by the impact of a giant asteroid or comet.

Kasei Vallis   Valley on Mars, 1,500 miles long and 200 miles wide believed to have been formed by one or more ancient floods.

kelvin (K)   Unit of temperature. A difference of one kelvin is the same difference as one degree Celsius. To convert kelvin to degrees Celsius, subtract 273.15.

Large Magellanic Cloud (LMC)   One of two irregular "satellite" galaxies (the other is the Small Magellanic Cloud) to our own, each about 100,000 light years away. They are only visible from the southern hemisphere and were first noted by navigator Ferdinand Magellan in 1519.

light   Portion of the spectrum of electromagnetic radiation visible to the human eye. The least energetic visible light is red, beyond which is infrared. The most energetic is violet, beyond which is ultraviolet.

light year   Distance light travels (at 186,000 miles per second) in one Earth year in a vacuum, approximately 6 trillion miles.

Local Group   Cluster of about 40 galaxies of which our own galaxy, the Milky Way, is a member. It is dominated by two particularly large galaxies, our own and the Andromeda galaxy, M31.

Magellan mission   U.S. spacecraft placed in orbit around Venus in 1990. It produces high-resolution maps of the Venusian terrain by side-mapping radar.

maria   The fifteen percent of the moon's surface flooded over 3 billion years ago by molten lava. Maria appear darker and less cratered than the highlands.

Mariner probes   Highly successful series of U.S. spacecraft that conducted explorations of Venus, Mars, and Mercury between 1962 and 1975.

mass   Amount of matter in a body, roughly equivalent to the number of nucleons present.

Messier ("M") number   Number given to 103, then (in a revised list) 109 "nebulae," fuzzy cloud-like objects visible to the naked eye or low-powered telescope by Charles Messier. The original list was published in 1784. Most objects turned out to be galaxies (e.g., M31, the Andromeda galaxy) and clusters of stars, while some (e.g., M42, the Orion nebula) are true nebulae, glowing clouds of gas in our own galaxy.

meteor (shooting star)   Streak of light in the night sky caused by an interplanetary particle of dust (or larger, up to about the size of a small pebble) burning itself out in Earth's atmosphere at an altitude of between about 40 and 80 miles and at a velocity of up to 150,000 mph. The light we see comes mainly from a hot "channel" of ionized air around the particle.

meteor shower   Annual occurrence when Earth passes through a "meteor stream" of dust sublimated from the surface of a comet, e.g., Perseids (August) and Geminids (December).

meteorite   "Stone from the sky." Interplanetary body large enough not to have been burnt up in the atmosphere. Meteorites are classified as stony, iron, or stony-iron. The vast majority are termed stony chondrites (stones containing chondrules, round masses of olivine or pyroxene). It's estimated that over three thousand meteorites hit Earth each year. Thousands have been found and classified.

micron   One millionth of a meter. (A meter is about $39^{1}/_{2}$ inches.)

Milky Way   (1) Broad, pale swath of light, resolved into individual stars by binoculars or a telescope, visible on moonless nights from dark location. This is our view of our own galaxy seen edge-on to us. (2) Our galaxy (what used to be termed the Galaxy), a conglomeration of between 100 and 400 billion stars held together by mutual gravitational attraction. Most hot, bright stars are found in spiral arms in the Milky Way's disk. "Globular clusters," consisting mainly of older stars, lie in a roughly spherical "halo" centered on the central nucleus. The Milky Way is about 100,000 light years across. Our sun lies about 30,000 light years from the nucleus, on the inner edge of one of the spiral arms. In addition to the visible portion, it's believed ninety percent (or even ninety-nine percent) of our galaxy is not only invisible, but is composed of "dark matter" of (at present) unknown material. (Our galaxy looks similar to M31, C-1.)

minor planet   See *asteroid*.

moon   Body in orbit around a planet. The moon (or Moon) is Earth's natural satellite, a body having about one eightieth the mass, and one quarter the diameter, of Earth. It orbits us at a distance of about one quarter of a million miles, with the same hemisphere always facing Earth.

NASA   National Aeronautics and Space Agency, U.S. civilian agency formed in 1958 having responsibility for the (nonmilitary) space program.

nebula   Cloud of interstellar gas and dust in our galaxy. Bright (subdivided into emission and reflection) nebulae are luminous (e.g., the Orion nebula). Dark nebulae are cooler clouds (e.g., the Horsehead nebula) silhouetted by bright nebulae. Many dust clouds eventually accrete into stars.

Nemesis hypothesis   Proposal advanced by Richard Muller and others, that if mass extinctions took place on a regular basis (about every 26 million years) as proposed in 1983 by David Raup and John Sepkoski, the causative agent is a star in an eccentric 26 million-year orbit about the sun. When the star, dubbed "Nemesis," gets close to the sun it disturbs comets in the Oort Cloud, sending many sunward, where some eventually collide with Earth, triggering extinctions.

neutron   Elementary atomic particle found in atom's nucleus, approximately equal in mass to the proton. It has no charge.

nucleons   Constituents of atomic nucleus, protons and neutrons.

nucleus   Central part. Of an atom, the part consisting of nucleons. Of a comet, the solid core. Of our galaxy, comparatively dense bulge in the disk of the Milky Way.

Olympus Mons   Martian volcano, and highest known volcano in the solar system. (See C-8.)

Oort Cloud   Hypothetical "cloud" of millions or billions of comets in orbit around the sun at distances up to 100,000 AU. Any disturbances to this cloud result in some comets slowing up and falling in towards the sun, where they might end up as short-period comets.

perihelion   Point at which an object in solar orbit is closest to the sun.

photon   Quantum, or smallest possible amount, of electromagnetic radiation.

photosphere   Visible "surface" of the sun, seen as a disk from Earth.

Pioneer mission   Series of U.S. solar-system probes, including the venerable Pioneers 10 and 11, the first spacecraft to reach Jupiter (both, 1973–74) and Saturn (Pioneer 11, 1979).

planet   One of nine large bodies (compared with the asteroids) in orbit around the sun, i.e., Mercury, Venus, Earth, Mars, Jupiter, Saturn, Uranus, Neptune, and Pluto (in order from the sun, although Pluto periodically comes inside Neptune's orbit). Other stars are presumed to have planets, but none have so far been directly detected. "Planet" comes from the ancient Greek word for "wanderer."

planetisimals   Material from which the planets formed by accretion in the early solar system. Their size ranges from dust to boulders many miles across.

prograde   Counterclockwise direction of orbit seen from "above", direction planets move around sun.

prominence   Solar feature, an arch or loop of incandescent gas reaching high above the photosphere. Normally seen through filters, prominences are visible during a total eclipse as fiery pink appendages on the edge of the eclipsed sun's disk. (See Fig. 2-2 and C-2.)

proton   Elementary atomic particle found in atom's nucleus. It is positively charged, with a mass approximately equal to that of the neutron and almost 2,000 times that of the electron.

red giant   Late stage in the evolution of a normal star following depletion of hydrogen fuel in the core, resulting in a bloated, cooler star than the original. Eventually the outer layers are lost to space and, in less massive stars like the sun, a small dense core called a white dwarf is left.

refraction, atmospheric   Phenomenon that causes celestial objects to be slightly higher in the sky than they actually are. You can see the same effect in the "bending" of a pencil in a glass of water.

satellite   The terms "satellite" and "moon" are interchangeable for natural bodies. The term satellite is often used for artificial bodies, e.g., Landsat and communication satellites.

shooting star   See *Meteor.*

sling-shot mechanism   See *Gravitational assist.*

SNC ("Snick")   Class of meteorites, eight in all (at the time of this writing), probably of planetary origin. Mars is thought by many astronomers to be the source. (See Figs. 6-8, 6-9.)

solar system   The sun and all bodies bound to it by gravitational attraction.

solstice   Moment when the sun reaches its farthest point overhead north or south of the equator. The summer and winter solstices are on or about June 21 and December 21. (See Fig. 3-8.)

star   Massive gaseous body that generates energy through thermonuclear fusion. All that's needed is sufficient mass: a mass equivalent to about 80 Jupiters automatically creates a sufficiently high density, hence temperature, at its core for nuclear fusion to start.

sun   Name we give to our star.

sunspot   Comparatively cool areas on the photosphere of the sun, where lines of intense magnetic force pierce the "surface." Sunspots usually appear in groups, and might last for weeks or even months. (See Fig. 2-3.)

synchronous rotation   Common phenomenon in solar system, whereby a moon always presents the same face to the planet it's orbiting, e.g., our moon always shows the same face to Earth. It's caused by tides raised by the planet's gravity, which knead the moon and thereby dissipate the "spin energy." This energy eventually reaches a minimum when the moon is in synchronous rotation. It's mutual: Earth's rotation, for instance, is being slowed down by tidal effects from our moon.

telescope Instrument to apparently (1) bring far objects closer and/or (2) make faint objects brighter (by concentrating light). Planetary observers are usually more interested in (1), where the objects are relatively bright. "Deep-space" observers are more concerned with (2), so they can examine faint objects.

terraform To convert a planet (or moon) into a terrestrial-like one. Mars is the best candidate for terraforming, where it consists of two basic components: (1) creating a climate rich in carbon dioxide suitable for plants (something like Earth over three billion years ago); (2) converting that into a climate on which humans can live unencumbered by oxygen bottles, ultraviolet protectors etc.

terrestrial planets—Mercury, Venus, Earth, and Mars: small rocky planets with shallow atmospheres (compared with Jupiter, Saturn, Uranus, and Neptune).

Tharsis Ridge Feature on Mars, principal location of the planet's volcanic activity. It includes Mars' largest volcanoes: Olympus Mons, Arsia Mons, Ascraeus Mons, and Pavonis Mons.

tidal effect Distortion of one body by another as a result of differential gravitational pull. For instance, when the moon is overhead, its mass exerts maximum gravitational pull where you are, and least on the opposite side of Earth. So where you are bulges slightly towards the moon, while the opposite side of Earth is "left behind." Oceans, being fluid, are more subject to tidal effects than solid rock.

universe Everything. Usually applied to the visible universe, that part of the entire universe about which we can possibly have any knowledge (light from beyond the visible universe will never reach us due to the expansion).

Valles Marineris The "canyonlands" of Mars, a great 2,500 mile-long system of trenches lying just south of the Martian equator with maximum width of 400 miles and depth of 4 miles. (See Fig. 4-5.)

Venera program Soviet series of space probes to Venus, including eight landers, most of which sent back pictures from the surface in the brief time (up to about two hours) they survived the high surface temperature.

Viking mission Two identical U.S. spacecraft whose landers soft-landed on Mars in 1976 and transmitted back photographs and data from life-seeking experiments. The Viking orbiters, meanwhile, mapped the planet in much greater detail than had been done by the previous Mariner spacecraft.

volcano Vent in the crust of a planet or moon through which magma, gas, dust, lava etc. are expelled; and the resulting conical structure. Volcanoes have been found on Earth, Venus, Mars, Io, and Triton. Hawaii consists of shield volcanoes, low flattened domes formed from flows of very fluid lava.

Voyager mission Two identical U.S. probes launched in 1977 towards Jupiter and, subsequently, Saturn. After passing close to Saturn's rings, Voyager 1 headed out of the plane of the solar system. Voyager 2 went on to Uranus (1986) and Neptune (1989).

weight Force experienced by a body as a result of the gravitational attraction of another.

white dwarf Small, dense, dying star, with a mass less than 1.4 times that of the sun, which has undergone gravitational collapse at the end of the red giant stage.

Index

Other Bestsellers of Related Interest

**EXPLORING CHEMICAL ELEMENTS AND THEIR COMPOUNDS
—David L. Heiserman**

Written for everyone who needs a solid introduction to the elements, this detailed guide presents a comprehensive summary of each element's properties and characteristics, scientific and commercial applications, compounds and isotopes, and historical background. Plus, throughout the book you'll find fascinating chemical trivia. 382 pages, 436 illustrations. **Book No. 3760, $17.95** paperback, **$26.95** hardcover

**GENETICS: The Mystery & the Promise
—Francis Leone**

Have you ever wondered why you are unique, why there isn't another person in the whole world exactly like you? In this intriguing book, you'll be transported into the world of genes, chromosomes, and the fantastically complex molecules that comprise the essence of life. You'll get a clear sense of how genetic research has changed the course of science in the past, and how it's likely to alter the future. 240 pages, 59 illustrations. **Book No. 3638, $14.95** paperback only

VIOLENT STORMS—Jon Erickson

This book provides up-to-date information on recurring atmospheric disturbances. The internal and external mechanisms that cause weather on the Earth and the way these forces come together to produce our climate are examined. Many photographs, line drawings, and tables, as well as a complete glossary make this engrossing book informative, entertaining, and easy to read. 240 pages, 190 illustrations. **Book No. 2942, $16.95** paperback only

GREENHOUSE EARTH: Tomorrow's Disaster Today—Jon Erickson

Depletion of the ozone layer . . . ocean dumping . . . destruction of the rain forest . . . all of these contribute to the deadly buildup of carbon dioxide in the Earth's atmosphere. This important book clearly explains what's happening to the land, sea, and atmosphere because of pollution. It identifies the many sources of atmospheric carbon dioxide and explains how the gas reacts with other pollutants to lock in the Earth's heat. 176 pages, 125 illustrations. **Book No. 3471, $14.95** paperback, **$22.95** hardcover

THE NEW EXPLORER'S GUIDE TO MAPS AND COMPASSES—Percy W. Blandford

Written especially for children ages 8 and up, this is a complete guide to understanding, reading, and using maps and compasses. Filled with activities, it teaches valuable skills such as identifying latitude and longitude: reading map symbols, abbreviations, and scales; setting a map or compass and orienteering by them; planning a trip using a map; or making a map for a journey through the wilderness. 160 pages, 67 illustrations. **Book No. 3859, $7.95** paperback, **$15.95** hardcover

WORLD OUT OF BALANCE: Our Polluted Planet—Jon Erickson

In this sobering picture of what pollution and overpopulation have done to the biosphere, you'll discover the global consequences of pollution and see how fragile the balance of nature has become. This historical perspective begins with the origin of life and concludes with many thought-provoking projections about the future of the planet. 176 pages, 125 illustrations. **Book No. 3963, $14.95** paperback, **$22.95** hardcover

THROUGH THE TELESCOPE: A Guide for the Amateur Astronomer
—Michael R. Porcellino

Through the Telescope is an open invitation to explore our universe. This book and an amateur astronomical telescope are all you need to meet the multitude of stars, nebulae, and deep-sky objects that can be seen on a dark, clear night. Porcellino guides you on a tour of the Moon, where you'll visit craters, mountains and niles, and learn to identify their unique features. Next you'll move out to the satellites of Jupiter, the rings of Saturn, and the Sun. 352 pages, 217 illustrations. **Book No. 3159, $18.59** paperback only

LIGHT, LASERS AND OPTICS
—John H. Mauldin

A fascinating introduction to the science and technology of modern optics. Broad enough to appeal to the general science enthusiast, yet technically specific enough for the experienced electronics hobbyist, this book fully explains the science of optics. You'll explore: everyday observations on light, the theory and physics of light and atoms, computing with light, optical information storage, and many other related subjects! *Light, Lasers and Optics* is extremely well illustrated with over 200 line drawings. 240 pages, 205 illustrations. **Book No. 3038, $16.95** paperback only

THE SECRET LIFE OF QUANTA
—Dr. M.Y. Han; Foreword by Eugen Merzbacher, Ph.D.

Now your questions about high-tech physics are answered in plain, low-tech English. When you try to find out exactly *why* atoms do what they do, you'll find that many of the texts are written for physicists, not for the reader who is simply curious. That's what makes this such an important publishing milestone. This is your handbook for the 21st century. 198 pages, 103 illustrations. **Book No. 3397, $12.95** paperback, **$17.95** hardcover

TARGET EARTH!: Asteroid Collisions Past and Future—Jon Erickson

Since the beginning of time, asteroids have been colliding with Earth. It is now generally accepted that the impact of large asteroids produced geological and climatological changes that led to the extinction of the dinosaurs millions of years ago. Is the Earth due for another such collision? *Target Earth!: Asteroid Collisions Past and Future* investigates what asteroids are, where they come from, and how their collisions with the Earth have affected our planet. You'll also see what scientists are doing to protect the Earth from asteroids, and learn how asteroids could be mined or used as outposts for space exploration. 184 pages, 141 illustrations. **Book No. 3673, $14.95** paperback, **$23.95** hardcover

MAPS AND COMPASSES—2nd Edition—Percy W. Blandford

This guide is for all who frequently find themselves in unfamiliar territory. Assuming no prior knowledge, Blandford explains in clear, illustrated detail how to interpret and use all kinds of maps, charts, and compasses when traveling on land and water. You'll learn how to read scale proportions and find out what symbols are found on land maps, nautical maps, topographic maps, and road maps. And for your reference, there is a listing of the most common conventional symbols used in the legends of most maps. 288 pages, 215 illustrations. **Book No. 3838, $14.95** paperback, **$22.95** hardcover

Look for These and Other TAB Books at Your Local Bookstore

To Order Call Toll Free 1-800-822-8158
(in PA, AK, and Canada call 717-794-2191)

or write to TAB BOOKS, Blue Ridge Summit, PA 17294-0840.

Title	Product No.	Quantity	Price

☐ Check or money order made payable to TAB BOOKS

Charge my ☐ VISA ☐ MasterCard ☐ American Express

Acct. No. _____ Exp. _____

Signature: _____

Name: _____

Address: _____

City: _____

State: _____ Zip: _____

Subtotal $ _____

Postage and Handling
($3.00 in U.S., $5.00 outside U.S.) $ _____

Add applicable state and local
sales tax $ _____

TOTAL $ _____

TAB BOOKS catalog free with purchase; otherwise send $1.00 in check or money order and receive $1.00 credit on your next purchase.

Orders outside U.S. must pay with international money order in U.S. dollars.

TAB Guarantee: If for any reason you are not satisfied with the book(s) you order, simply return it (them) within 15 days and receive a full refund.
                                                                        BC